What People Are Saying
About the Harmonic Egg

"My experience in the Egg was extraordinary. I felt happy in my heart as soon as I saw it, but then the experience of being in it and taking the healing journey it offers was profound. I didn't want to speak afterward and needed 20 minutes or so to feel ready to leave the building and engage with the outside world. I felt peaceful, rearranged and reconnected. Gail Lynn is a beautiful soul who has created a brilliant device for the world—and I am immensely grateful."

— **LEE HARRIS**, Spiritual Teacher and Speaker, Channel, Energy Guide, and author of *Energy Speaks*. leeharrisenergy.com

"An aspect of my work over the last 40 years has been researching the effects of sacred geometry on our physical, emotional, and spiritual bodies. Just seeing the geometric shape, before even entering the Harmonic Egg, I could immediately feel the uplifting energy in the room. I also perceived how my body felt an immediate calmness upon seeing it."

— **STEVEN A. ROSS**, Ph.D., President, World Research Foundation.

"I came to the Life Center because, for the last 20-plus years, I have been supporting the integration of children diagnosed with autism, and others who experience heightened sensory sensitivities. In January 2019, I started to receive information from this population that there was a 'pod' that could help with their integration. I met Gail through a mutual friend and immediately knew that this is what the children had been talking about. I flew to Denver from LA and had two back-to-back sessions.

During my first session in the Harmonic Egg (HE), I entered with the intention to determine if this was the 'pod' the children were talking about. During this session, something was immediately cleared from my third eye and a symbol of balance was placed in my heart! I then heard children laughing and saw a giant tree of life with Harmonic Eggs hanging below the leaf line and above the ground. The Harmonic Eggs slowly descended and children walked out onto the earth! I took this as a sign that the HE could help this population be here.

The second session, I did for myself and especially for the integration of the child and the parent within me! My own integration of past trauma and disconnection is what led me to finding means for integration in the first place. In this session, I saw my biological parents as well as myself at various ages during my childhood. I fell asleep in the session, which, for me, tells me I am 'going deep.' On returning home, I found myself very tired for at least a couple days. I took that as a sign of integration!

The real magic occurred a week later.

Prior to meeting Gail, I had scheduled a trip to go see my mother. I was open to the experience, but nervous about it, because there has been a distance in our relationship for decades. However, this experience was completely different! My mother and I laughed and enjoyed each other's company. My defenses seemed to drop naturally. I could feel her love for me, and mine was genuine toward her. The child in both of us acknowledged how much we missed each other. The reason for the distancing just seemed non-existent.

Given my experience in the Harmonic Egg, and my request, I know that it was this experience that helped heal this dynamic. After just two sessions, it brought the parent and child within me closer together. It did the same for my mother and me. If this level of connection can be made for me, I have no doubt that beautiful connections can be made for those on the spectrum through the Harmonic Egg!"

— SUZY MILLER, Visionary Speaker, Teacher, Energy Guide
and Founder and author of *Awesomism: A New Way to
Understand the Diagnosis of Autism*. Suzymiller.com

Unlocking
The Ancient Secrets
To Healing

Why Science Is Looking To The Past
For The Future Of Medicine

Gail Lynn

Disclaimer

The statements made by the author and any recommendations of services in this book are not intended to diagnose, treat, cure or prevent any disease. Testimonials regarding the technology are voluntarily given and do not represent the opinions of the author. The information provided and knowledge and experiences shared by the author are not intended to be a substitute for professional medical advice, diagnosis, or treatment.

ISBN 978-1-7343783-0-6

Printed and bound in the United States by Kingery Printing Company.

10 9 8 7 6 5 4 3 2

Edited by Sandra Sedgbeer
Cover design and interior layout by Damian Keenan
Author photo by Rebecca Sederberg, www.alltheabovephotography.com
This book was typeset in Adobe Garamond Pro, Calluna Sans, with ITC Century Std Book Condensed used as display typefaces

You can get in touch with the author of this book using the contact form on her website at **www.harmonicegg.com**

Contents

Foreword
By Dr. Dominique Surel

As an MBA with a Doctoral degree and international consulting experience, my background would be regarded as very much fitting the mainstream model. Indeed, I have always been extremely skeptical about anything outside the mainstream. Thus, I had little time for or belief in anything that could not be scientifically proven.

However, I've also had a parallel life and career. One which, initially, I was almost unwilling to embark on. This parallel career, which led me to become a radiesthésiste and a practitioner of Controlled Remote Viewing (CRV), resulted from a journey of discovery I took into the realm of the non-local.

Radiesthesia is the ancient Egyptian and Hermetic science of operating with invisible frequencies in the non-local realm. The premise is that the human body and soul is merely an instrument that can be fine-tuned to recognize and operate in the non-local. Radiesthesia also teaches the complex science that specific forms and shapes emit different energetic patterns that can be either beneficial or harmful or can also amplify or decrease another frequency. Although there are many French books written about the topic, the actual operational methodology is still, today, passed down by word of mouth.

In the 1980s, I was living in Paris, fully engaged in my mainstream career. At that time, I had never even heard of Radiesthesia or Controlled Remote Viewing, let alone considered studying it. And then I met an engineer, Doctor GF who had continued his studies to become a physician and homeopath. Doctor GF, was looking for someone to whom he could pass on his knowledge. And for some reason, he chose me. It seemed strange to me because I was such a stoic skeptic... until he asked me to hold a pendulum and gave me instructions on what to do. Being French, I was very polite and decided to go through the motions, and then go home! To my utmost surprise, the pendulum moved on its own, and at the same time, a sort of door flung open into what I later learned was the non-local realm. I could feel, both physically and mentally, that I had entered into a new world that was undeniably real. My reaction was simple: I exploded into uncontrollable laughter, and for maybe five minutes, both GF and I could not stop laughing.

That was the beginning of my full-time two-year training with GF in radiesthesia and other parallel sciences of the invisible realm. The first application I learned was in homeopathy, and how, for each disease, different homeopathic remedies and dilutions are needed for different people depending upon their overall health terrain. At the end of the two years, I was registered at the local homeopathic pharmacy and was able to request specific dilutions. GF also demonstrated how he could heal cancer and how it all worked. My life was never the same after this experience.

Years later, I moved to the USA, where I felt there was something else that I needed to learn. I happened to read about Controlled Remote Viewing (CRV). CRV is a protocol that was researched and developed by the US military to tap into the human's natural propensity to access non-local information. In other words, psychic skills. An individual is given a set of randomly selected numbers and or letters that label a specific place or event (the target). By following an exact protocol, and without having any idea of what the target is, the individual will then "go there" and record their impressions at the target. When I first read about this, I immediately chuckled and discounted the entire concept. No way could this be possible. But as time passed, my mind was stuck on CRV—I kept thinking about it and dismissing it. Finally, tired of CRV occupying so much time in my thoughts, I decided to sign-up for training with one of the best military CRV specialists: Lyn Buchanan. My purpose was to prove to myself that this was not possible and get it out of my mind.

In CRV, the protocol is quite simple and entails just sitting at a desk, fully awake with no preparation, with pen and paper, just recording information. As I prepared to "view" my very first target, Lyn was sitting next to me, making sure I was following the protocol. I started to write things that came through my mind: open space, water, slight wind. At this point, I looked up from my paper to see if a window was open because I felt the wind on my face, but Lyn said, "Just write it down." Finally, I had nothing else coming through and told Lyn, "I'm done."

"No, you are not," was his answer.

"Yes, I am," I retorted." By now, I was tired and embarrassed about not having any feeling of being at the target. I just wanted to leave and have a nice glass of wine, when, out of nowhere, I heard Lyn say in a loud voice,

"Why are you rocking back and forth on your chair?"

That totally interrupted my dream-like thoughts, and I found myself replying, "Because I'm on a—"

"Write it down. NOW!" Lyn barked at me. I was so stunned by his command that I thought to myself he wants me to write something? Fine, I will. I'll just make up something, whatever comes to my mind, so I can get out of here. So, I wrote, "I am on a sailboat. It is a spring day, with a light breeze, and the sailboat is rocking on its side. It's warm, and in the background is a beach with a hill." There, I thought. Here's my story. Can I go have a glass of wine now?

With a smirk on his face, Lyn said, "Do you want to see the photo of the target?"

No!!! Of course, I do not. I know I did not describe it at all. I've already embarrassed myself beyond imagination. It's ok. I don't want to see it. Lyn showed it to me anyway. The photo showed a sailboat leaning to one side, with a beach and a hill in the background. People were dressed as if it were early summer. I was speechless. How does this work?

After 30 years of practicing radiesthesia, and twenty years of practicing and teaching CRV, I learned a great deal about how the human instrument (i.e., us) can develop itself to operate in the non-local realm. I developed my own protocol to elicit our natural intuition skills so that we can determine the difference between imagined information (and wishful-thinking) versus true, non-local information or accurate intuition.

Operating effectively in the non-local realm takes a lifetime of continuous practice and learning. The transformational process stipulates the dissolution of the ego. The more humility one has, the more knowledge is revealed. One rule that is common to radiesthesia, hermetics, alchemy, and CRV is that the more grounded and awake (conscious) you are, the easier it will be to establish an accurate connection to the non-local. Meditation can be not only a distraction but an invitation for the conscious mind to fulfil wishful thinking by manifesting a scenario, which features all the senses such as smells, colors, tactical feelings, etc., and thus producing an experience that might be interpreted as true or very real even though it is manifested only in the creative part of the intellect. Discerning between authentic connections and the advanced manipulations of the conscious mind can take a lifetime of training. That said, some individuals are born with a naturally strong connection to the non-local. But such people are very, very rare. They are usually very humble and do not seek recognition.

Which brings me to the reason why I accepted Gail's invitation to write this foreword.

Over the last few decades, entitlement has become a form of social disease. This mentality has become rampant and has even invaded the realm of spirituality, and, more dangerously, the field of alternative medicine. It has created a vast community of individuals who "wanna be" recognized as offering something special. They wake up one morning and might decide they are healers. Or they decide to invent some energetic miracle machine or instrument with the idea that "If Joe can channel something, so can I." The conscious mind is quite powerful, and research from neuropsychologist Paul Pearsall, amongst others, demonstrates that it is structured and programmed to make our goals come true. If one strongly wishes to channel some information, the conscious mind, aided by one's intelligence and creativity, will manifest a realistic scenario and give credence to one's wishful thinking. The result is that we find ourselves overwhelmed with all types of healing methodologies and machines, some of which are grounded in measurable results while most others are not.

How can we discern what works and what doesn't?

I met Gail Lynn when she contacted me to take my private CRV training. I am very selective about teaching CRV, as I do not want to teach this powerful methodology to just anyone. Gail immediately impressed me with her grounded and intelligent questions. I found her to be refreshing compared to many of the new-agers that I seem to attract. As Gail embarked on learning CRV, I found that she immediately understood each principle and also had a natural connection to the non-local realm. During breaks, we continued discussing the invisible but real world. Then Gail declared that she wanted to take all my trainings - "Radiesthesia, intuitive intelligence, and, is there anything else?" Gail was so serious and passionate, it touched my heart. She took all the trainings I offered, and I was continuously surprised at how quickly she learned and understood the depth and applications. I remember asking her whether she hadn't learned this with someone else. Her focus on developing accuracy and discerning between possible imagination versus pure intuition and non-local information duly impressed me. I felt that she was actually continuously plugged into the non-local but had not realized it. Unlike many of our contemporary colleagues who "want to be," Gail truly was —and in such an unassuming way. No ego, just concern about quality and accuracy. How refreshing!

One day, Gail said she wanted to share something with me. She was thinking of creating a healing chamber in the form of an egg, using colored light and music. She had spent many years researching healing using light and sound, as well as the qualities of the shape of an egg. Her passion and knowledge about combining these three elements (light, sound, egg) were contagious. The discussion(s) that ensued was almost a bit strange. Although Gail confided that she really didn't know where she was going with this, the more I questioned her, the more I realized that she *did* know what she was talking about. It was as if she had this concept in her mind with all the details, but did not even know it was there! At the end of our conversations, she almost seemed surprised herself at the amount of information that was uncovered.

It was clear to me that Gail was indeed "channeling" the schematic of this Egg. Other individuals had come to me with supposedly channeled ideas and explained how they would be able to not only heal but raise the consciousness of other people. But it has been evident to me that none of it was channeled, and aspiring to raise the consciousness of others is a rather ego-generated and presumptuous idea. Gail, on the other hand, was very matter-of-fact with no ego-generated statements. I could tell that she was delivering pure information in its essence, with no human emotion attached to it, only diligence in going back to the drawing board to make it perfect. It is rare to witness someone genuinely channeling, and I was grateful to see such a unique event. When we discussed the potential of actually helping people with medical issues, her persona would light-up with pure joy—no ego.

As time passed, Gail worked diligently on her design. She would send me drafts of what she was working on. And using my radiesthesia skills with the pendulum, I would test it against the outcome characteristics that we had discussed and made suggestions as to changes. I also incorporated some of the alchemical principles that I had learned with GF to ensure that the harmony created by the three elements of Shape, Sound, and Color would resonate and create its own fluid healing entity at a higher level. Meanwhile, Gail continued working with the sacred science of geometry, and each iteration of the Egg was an improvement on the last.

As we quickly progressed, I could feel the design of the Egg taking on its unique dimensions or shape. At one point, I felt it beginning to take on a biological quality of its own. In a later iteration of Gail's design, I realized that the Egg could regulate its healing diffusion of sound and light, depending on who was sitting in it! That's when it also became evident that intention was playing a critical role in the creation of the Egg. Not just Gail's and my intention, but also the intention of anyone else involved in the creative process. As usual, Gail immediately got it.

It had also been clear to me from the beginning of our collaboration that Gail has an intuitive skill in selecting the precise pieces of music for healing with the appropriate colors. But as with any intuitive skill, to be accurate, knowledge plays an important part. Gail has spent many years studying the healing power of both sound and colors. She explored concepts from around the world and has come up with her own method of synchronizing sound with colors. At the beginning of our collaboration, I would ask her detailed questions about how she did it. I discovered that after having created a solid base of knowledge, the synchronization is done through her intuitive channel. Again, it is part of her channeling of the Egg. But I also believe she has access to it because she has done the "work." This is something I learned earlier on about intuition and channeling; one cannot "decide" to download or channel information for it to happen. One needs to make an effort or work to educate oneself to acquire a deep understanding of the science before the whole picture is accessible.

Fast-forward a few months, and the Harmonic Egg was born and effectively functioning, bringing relief and healing to some seriously ill patients. Some of these experiences are shared in this book.

Although I had helped Gail develop the qualities of the Egg, when it was time for me to experience it the skeptic in me was unsure of what to expect. It was one thing to work with the Egg on paper, but to actually experience it in the manifested form of the material world was something else entirely. Within just a few minutes, I felt as if the colors and sounds were playing with the shape of the Egg, almost as an elegant game of physics. I could feel the waves of color and sound bouncing off the interior of the Egg. Sitting inside the Egg, the interaction felt playful but with intention. And then, all of a sudden, I felt that I had become a fourth and intricate element of this interaction. It translated into a harmonic energy that I could feel at the cellular level! It was warm, light, purposeful, and amazing. Although I was conscious of time, it had taken on an ethereal quality and become totally irrelevant. When the session was finished, I felt light and almost giddy, just as I had when the door to the nonlocal had flung open while testing the pendulum with GF.

This personal experience of the Harmonic Egg demonstrated to me that it does calibrate with the specific human energy sitting inside of it. The Egg takes on its biological quality when a human is present, and, in my estimation, does a swift scan before working on re-stabilizing a weakness in the health terrain of the human. This is when intention plays an active role in where the Harmonic Egg waves of energy will focus - not just the intention that was placed in the selection of music and light, but also the intention of the human sitting inside the Egg.

As the medical world is slowly evolving toward energy medicine, the other sciences, such as physics, are discovering some of the basic concepts of radiesthesia and alchemy. For example, scientists such as Bohm recognize that there is another realm whereby subatomic particles remain in contact or entangled with one another regardless of distance or time. Yet, they are not sending signals or traveling because there is no time or space in that realm. The Harmonic Egg operates in that realm, which exists but is not yet totally explained by modern science.

Until then, Gail's Harmonic Egg is one of the rare instruments today that works in that realm with measurable healing results. The Harmonic Egg operates energetically and harmonically at the cellular level. It appears to reach a depth that conventional medicine cannot tap into. A major part of its success is that, after gaining critical knowledge over many years, Gail created the Harmonic Egg with humility, integrity, and pure intention. I am grateful to have had the opportunity to share my own knowledge in such an exceptional and meaningful enterprise.

Dominique Surel,
Colorado, 2020

Dominique Surel, PhD., MBA is a Noetic scholar, who specializes in the development of intuitive intelligence. She is an international invited speaker and Dean of Faculty and Professor at Energy Medicine University (EMU, California) where she teaches Critical Thinking, Intuitive Intelligence, Leadership, and Controlled Remote Viewing. NoeticSI.com

Dedication

To my friend, lover, meal buddy,
and soul traveler, Bill.

BABE, you have put up with all my stress, and tried to solve all the problems I encountered. For all the late nights I spent working when you selflessly thought of me and only me; when you made me hundreds of meals and sent me home with hundreds of leftovers, so I didn't skip eating. And the millions of texts you sent, making sure I was drinking enough water and remembering to eat, so I didn't get sick. You sat on the sidelines and cheered me on for many years now.

I could never express my gratitude and appreciation for all you have done to support me on this journey. You are my rock, and my Viking warrior, allowing me to be the divine feminine.

I love you always.

TO MY BESTIE MOM, and my unassuming and practical Dad, may they both rest in peace, and know that I would not be the woman I am today without their love and teachings. I miss them every day—Mom's organization, and stubborn drive to make things happen, and Dad's creativity and common-sense approach to life were the perfect combinations for my journey.

Love you both to the ends of the universe!

TO MY BEAUTIFUL SISTER, GLORIA, who spent many years sharing a bedroom with me as a child. You may be younger, but you are a wise woman. I am so grateful for our talks and our laughs. No one on this earth makes me laugh harder than you. Thank you for being one of the best parts of my life.

I love you so much. Follow your intuition. Step into that power of yours. You make the world a better place.

AND, LASTLY, MY BROTHER, GARY. What can I say? We are finally reconnected after decades of estrangement. I am so happy to have you in my life again. You help me on so many levels to see things differently, and you are a lot like Dad in your approach to life.

Having you in my life makes me whole again. Love you, bro.

Let it Flow!
Gail

Introduction –
What Did I Sign Up For?!

The man in the wheelchair looks skeptical. I can't blame him. Suddenly my confidence is wavering too. I cannot let it show, of course. But from the moment my friend Wayman wheeled his friend TQ into my office, I've been aware of a nervous fluttering in my stomach.

This is it. I know it. This will be my proof that all the hard work, the sleepless nights studying and learning, the endless calculations, the drafting, and redrafting, not to mention the expense, were worth it.

If I can help this man, the absolute faith I have placed in the unknown source of information I've intuitively been receiving will be vindicated. Finally, I shall *know* that the unseen forces that have been guiding me through the labyrinthine passages of my life's journey have been doing so with a precise purpose.

Doubt and uncertainty declare their presence in the myriad subtle ways my body is responding to this moment. The sudden shift in the rhythm of my breathing... the way my heart is beating just a little bit faster behind my ribcage... the slight adjustment in my body temperature... the sensation of slickness on my fingertips...

Oh, Lord, I think, as my heart reaches out to this sad, ailing veteran as my psychic senses simultaneously scan his physical and emotional condition. *Grossly overweight. Heart condition. Kidneys look as though they're shutting down. Emotionally frozen. Holding on by a thread. I just don't know if he's beyond help.*

I rise from my chair, using the movement as cover for surreptitiously removing any trace of sweat from my hands by quickly smoothing down my pants. Hugging Wayman, I extend a hand to TQ and smile a few welcoming words. I am not going to patronize him. He trusts Wayman enough to come this far, but it is evident that he doesn't really believe I can help him. *And why should he?* I'm thinking. *Given what he's been through, and how it's still affecting him.*

Wayman had shared a few details about his friend TQ's situation when he'd called me the week before. "He's had severe PTSD for a long time." He'd confided. "It's still ongoing, and now the medical professionals at the VA are talking about dialysis for his failing kidneys. I'm worried that time might be running out for him…" Wayman had paused before startling me with his next admission. "… Just as it did for the other fourteen survivors."

"Survivors? What survivors?" I had blurted out, perplexed.

I'd heard the deep intake of breath, followed by the long, slow, almost defeated sigh. "TQ's unit was part of a big operation. Only fifteen soldiers out of the original 3,000 returned alive. The other survivors are all gone now. He's the last of them. I don't know what he experienced, he won't talk about it. But I know it was bad. You don't get PTSD from going on a picnic. Or survivor's guilt."

"That's awful," I'd breathed. "The poor man. I can't even begin to imagine what he's been through."

"I'd really like him to have some sessions in the Egg. If it can do for him what it's clearly doing for others…" Wayman's voice had trailed off. "Well… If the Egg can't help him… I don't think anything can. I'll bring him by next week."

I have been thinking about TQ a lot this past week. And of how Wayman's fear and his hope for his friend had colored the tone of his voice. Wayman knew better than most people what the Egg seemed to be capable of; he'd helped me build the first prototype. In the process, he'd unwittingly experienced some surprising physical benefits in his own body. But as research confirms, there are many factors involved in disease, two of the most important being the psyche and the emotions. And between what I've heard from Wayman, and what my intuition is telling, there is a lot of deeply-rooted emotional trauma and pain at the core of TQ's dire physical situation.

Although my background and initial training were in engineering and project management, events in my life steered me in some unexpected directions. In my eagerness to learn more about what makes us who we are, I had been drawn to study consciousness, vibrational energy, and frequency healing technologies and methodologies. Everything I read, learned, and experienced throughout my years of research and training led me ultimately to establish my own energy-based wellness center in Denver, Colorado.

A few years earlier, I had worked closely with and received training from a highly gifted inventor, one of, if not the first to harness the ancient, and now newly re-emerging, healing properties of sound, light, and color frequencies. With the aid of his groundbreaking device, I had recovered from several debilitating ailments and chronic conditions that had plagued my own health for more than two decades.

As innovative and effective as those "healing" devices had been, however, the engineer in me had identified some critical areas in which they could be improved upon. I was in the process of designing some upgrades to the technology when I was involved in a nasty automobile accident. Immediately after that, I had a sudden epiphany about combining sacred geometry and the golden ratio with light, sound, and color frequencies. Then I started receiving what I can only describe as "divine guidance." Before I knew it, I had developed a blueprint for a next-generation device, which I believed would create a paradigm shift in healing.

Utilizing my engineering and project management skills, Wayman helped me to create a prototype. Then I asked a remarkable woman, Dr. Dominique Surel, who teaches Radiesthesia and Controlled Remote Viewing (CRV) to cross-check and verify the correspondences in the harmonics.

Dr. Surel's expertise and feedback were instrumental in helping me build a geometrically balanced, dodecahedron, hollow egg-shaped chamber. I was ecstatic when tests revealed that the Egg's unique shape and combination of elements somehow stimulate the autonomic nervous system to release trauma at a cellular level, and promote a state of equilibrium in the body.

Since introducing three of these massive wooden chambers or Harmonic Eggs into my Center in Colorado, my staff and I have witnessed many incredible turnarounds in clients' physical, emotional, psychological, and mental health and well-being. Moreover, news about the Harmonic Egg's remarkable results is now reaching Wellness Centers throughout the USA and the world, many of which are purchasing their own Harmonic Eggs.

Despite all this, I still found it hard to believe that a regular girl like me from a blue-collar, Motown background could have helped build such an extraordinary device as the Harmonic Egg.

How many times have my friends reminded me that words like "impossible," "far-fetched," and "too good to be true" had been applied to other inventions that we now take for granted—citing electricity, television, radio, the telephone, the Internet, cellphones, and iWatches as examples? How many times have they faced me down with the question: "What's it gonna take for you to believe it?"

As if on cue, Wayman's call about TQ had given me the answer.

If the Harmonic Egg can effect a change in someone whose case seems as hopeless as TQ's... if it can help him avoid dialysis... and regain even a little better quality of life... if it can somehow help him find a way back from PTSD to a place where he can smile and have hope again... then I will have to believe it, I'd promised myself

Now here he is—my test case.

I mentally review TQ's state of physical health, along with the emotional trauma and psychological withdrawal that I believe are contributing to his decline. I am aware that I cannot offer him any guarantees or promises of recovery. Apart from being unethical and illegal, experience has taught me that healing is a co-creative process between the mind, the emotions, and the body. *Is the Harmonic Egg powerful enough to work on all three of TQ's energy bodies at the same time?*

Holding back tears of empathy for the years of mental and psychological suffering TQ must have endured, I gently ask him three critical questions. I need to determine first if he actually *wants* to get better. Second, if he *believes* he can get better. And third, how *much* he is willing to participate in accomplishing any improvements.

TQ's responses are initially listless and disinterested. But I press on. I don't ask about his diet; I can tell from the unhealthy appearance of his face, the fleshy girth of his body, and swollen limbs and fingers that fast foods, carbs, and sugar are his drugs of choice. Taking a deep breath, I make the decision to address TQ's problems head-on. No point in being anything less than frank. I look him in the eye.

"I'm going to be direct with you," I say. "And I want you to listen very carefully because I cannot stress this enough. I've seen some astonishing results with the Harmonic Egg. But if you want to start feeling better, you have to commit to working with me and with the Egg, not against us. I won't allow you to waste your money or my time with anything less than complete commitment. So, I'm laying down a few ground rules. The first of which concerns your diet."

The slight tightening of his mouth and increased tension in his body reveal that TQ doesn't like what he's hearing. Thankfully, Wayman immediately jumps in to block any resistance. He paints a graphic picture of what TQ's remaining years, or months, might look like if all the VA can offer him is dialysis. After several moments, TQ finally nods his head, saying that he will try to make an effort. It isn't quite the level of engagement that I am looking for, but it's a beginning. I walk over to the water machine, fill a glass up for each of us, and start talking about emotions and frequency.

"According to research, every emotion has a unique frequency," I say. "Negative emotions such as anger and fear vibrate at lower-frequency ranges while positive emotions such as love and joy vibrate at higher ranges. When trauma and grief occur in life, we tend to live in fear, anger, sadness, and other low-vibration emotions. The longer we stay in these low-frequency states of being, the more susceptible we are to disease and illness. To change our emotional state, we have to change our vibrational frequency."

Wayman nods his understanding. But TQ's face remains impassive. I can't tell if what I am saying is making any sense to him, but I continue regardless.

"Every organ in our body also has its own frequency, and certain organs resonate with the frequencies of specific emotions. When trauma or negative emotion gets suppressed or remains unresolved, that emotional frequency gets stored somewhere in our physical body and impedes our natural flow of energy. In some cases, the effects of this are instantaneous—a joint suddenly starts hurting without any apparent cause or injury, or a muscle goes into spasm, etc. In other cases, the stored emotion stays there and just gets added to as time goes on. Then, months or years later, the energy that is stuck in that organ, muscle, or area starts to manifest discomfort, dis-ease, or dysfunction. Correcting the emotional issues releases the tension in that area, which in turn frees the stuck energy to start flowing again. When it does, the affected organ or systems start recovering."

Though we've only been using the Egg a few months, we have sufficient evidence of its ability to help people break through old emotional patterns and create healthier ways of living. If the Egg can help TQ relax deeply enough, it will start freeing his body from the stress and fear that are constricting it. His body will then be able to start loosening the thick layer of emotional numbness that's keeping him detached from the fundamental life force—the will to live—which is the source of our well-being.

I hold this knowledge in my mind as I start preparing the chamber for TQ's first session. And, just as I do for every client, I set the intentions for him to experience whatever he is ready to receive for his well-being at this moment. The rest is up to the Egg, which, from my own and numerous clients' experiences, appears to have an uncanny ability to know and deliver precisely what each individual requires.

I am aware that entering the Harmonic Egg chamber for the first time can be a little unnerving for some people. So, I'm not surprised when TQ indicates this could be a problem for him. Luckily, Wayman comes to the rescue again and helps TQ maneuver his bulk into the chamber and get comfortably settled in the zero-gravity chair. "I'll just be outside," he says reassuringly. "I'll stay right there so, if you need me, you only have to shout."

I set the timer and return to my office, where my lunch is waiting for me. I ignore it and instead rest my head against my seat back for a few moments. I close my eyes and focus my attention for several moments on the intention I am holding for TQ. I think about all the times I've sat here, waiting for a new client to emerge from their first immersive experience in the Harmonic Egg, which many describe as "like being back in the womb."

Fleeting images cross my mind of the varied expressions of amazement I've seen on client's faces after their first experiences in the Egg... from wide-eyed astonishment and ear-to-ear grins to the speechless mumblings of those who quite literally can't find any words.... the memories bring tears of gratitude to my eyes.

For more than two years, the Harmonic Egg has occupied virtually every waking moment of my life. Although I, and others, refer to it as my invention, in all honesty, I don't feel right about taking all the credit for this astonishing feat of engineering. The role I played in piecing together and birthing this beautiful, bio-energetic, vibrational healing chamber into form was merely that of interpreter and facilitator for some higher consciousness that has graciously gifted us with the chamber for our healing.

A memory spontaneously surfaces. When I was younger, I used to think about how much more fun life would be if we could peek into the future. The gift of foresight would save us time, help us avoid mistakes, and sidestep failures. We would know just what to do and when to do it, and what we would need to succeed before we even started. But as I think about mistakes I've made, the pain and challenges I've experienced, my long-held dream to make a difference in the world, and my hopes for TQ, and all of my clients, I smile at the flaws in my childish thinking.

If I had owned a crystal ball back then, or at any point along the stumbling, twisty-turny journey that has led me to this particular moment in time, how might my experiences have been different?

What decisions might I have made to avoid the pain of failure, heartache, and mistakes... which I now know concealed my biggest spiritual lessons? Where would I be now if I had plotted my course safely in advance...

instead of allowing the mystery of life—some might call it fate—to guide me where my soul wanted me to be?

With age comes wisdom, or so it's said. The gift of hindsight has taught me that I didn't need a crystal ball to chart my course in life. My instincts and intuition—my internal GPS as I call them—knew where they were taking me all along. (It just took a while for me to catch on.) They led me into an engineering career, which prepared me with precisely the set of skills I would need. And challenging though they were, I now understand that none of the relationships I chose were mistakes or failures. For each gave me experiences and knowledge that shifted my perceptions, broadened my thinking, and contributed to my awakening. They also taught me that the hardest lessons and most difficult taskmasters are often our greatest teachers. The emotional stress and physical pain of those less than comfortable experiences propelled me to seek my own healing, to study and learn about subtle energy fields, the science of mind-body healing, and of frequency, sound, and light medicine. And the critical role that intention plays in every facet of our life, but especially in healing.

If I hadn't followed those pathways into the realms of the subtle and the unseen, I might never have developed the expertise and deep intuitive insights to become who I am today. When inspiration struck, I was equipped to be the co-creator of a revolutionary device that offers people like TQ a non-invasive way to release the stress and unblock the vital flow of energy in their physical bodies. I am finally fulfilling my dream to make a difference.

There are moments in life when, for whatever reason, the stars align in the heavens, and all the necessary aspects are in place for us to glimpse something that is so much bigger than ourselves. As I review the experiences, encounters, and people that played pivotal roles in shaping who I am, I am aware this is one of them. And I feel so much gratitude.

How could I complain about any of it? Every step, every moment, every challenge, every trauma and every triumph... which all brought me here to this pinnacle moment, where I can look at this incredible gift that I have been privileged to have a hand in creating.

And I am humbled.

PART I

Looking To The Past

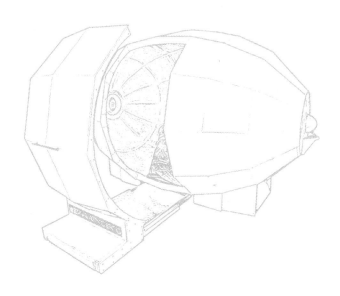

CHAPTER ONE

From Humble Beginnings

Like many children of working-class families in the early 1970s, life in Detroit, where I was born and raised, contained far more challenges than it did frills. I was the first of three children born to parents who were still very young themselves, and thus ill-equipped to be raising a family. My dad, who worked on an assembly line at the Ford Motor Company, was an alcoholic for most of my life. Money was tight, and every decision seemed to be driven by financial fear. Mom did several jobs to help support the family. Early on, she worked at night as a keypunch operator, later she worked at the public school doing payroll and accounting.

Looking back from this vantage point, I can see that I was pretty much in fight or flight mode from the get-go. I didn't remember a huge amount about my childhood until quite recently, but the memories I retained seem mostly to be unhappy ones; there was way more fighting and tension than laughter and hugs. I have heard that one emotional root of asthma is needing to be loved. I must have been missing something because I suffered from asthma from a very early age. One of my earliest memories is of being rushed to the hospital with a very severe asthma attack brought on by dandelions that I had picked for my kindergarten teacher. The nurses stabbed me so many times trying to get a blood sample that for decades, I came close to passing out any time I had to have blood drawn. I remember lying, terrified, on a bed in the hospital surrounded by what must have seemed to a four-year-old like an army of serious adults wielding scary looking instruments. I don't know why my mom was not allowed to stay with me, but hearing her loud sobs through the curtain that separated us only made me cry all the harder.

I guess it's not surprising that I was wary of adults. Most of those I knew weren't particularly kind or affectionate toward kids. I remember one New Year's Eve when I was about seven; Mom and Dad were going out to celebrate, so they got my dad's mom to come over and babysit. We didn't see her often and we were never close, so spending time with her wasn't something I looked forward to. The same must have applied to her because she spent the entire evening sleeping when she should have been watching us. I shook her at one point to see if she was okay. When she shrugged me off, saying she wasn't feeling too well, I got worried and called my parents. But when they came home, she accused me of lying. I overheard her telling them later when they were talking at the kitchen table that I was a manipulator and a liar. I was devastated to hear someone—my own grandmother—say such horrible things about me. The unfairness and humiliation of that stayed with me for years.

My best memories from childhood are mostly around softball. I was very athletic and started playing T-ball when I was seven. It soon became my life. I rode my bike to practice every day, and when I wasn't at practice, I practiced at home with friends. If I couldn't do either of those, I would just throw the ball in the air and catch it myself. One of our neighbors used to say that I was going to be the first professional woman baseball player because all I did was play baseball. I was so good at it that the coaches were always willing to go the extra mile for me. If a game were too far away for me to get to by bike, they would pick me up. And if I didn't get handed the number three shirt, which was my favorite number, they would rush to persuade whoever had it to swap with me. I couldn't explain what was so special about the number three, there was just something about it that felt "right" to me. Since learning about numerology and the energetic frequencies of numbers, I understand why I intuitively resonated with the number three.

I spent a lot of time on ball fields, which was where I felt the most confident and safe. I umpired T-ball games for younger kids, coached my little sister's softball team, and helped the coaches out whenever I could. Since my parents didn't come to many games to watch me play, I spent a lot of time with my coaches, who I looked up to and admired. They were my real role models, both the men and the women. And I continued to play some form of softball for 30 years.

I don't recall too much about school, other than I didn't like it, and I didn't do too well; I got mostly C's and D's in eighth grade. It was a strict Catholic school, where we had to wear a uniform. Mom was reluctant to overstretch the budget buying clothes that she didn't think we needed, so we only got one non-uniform outfit a year. Once I reached my teens, I wanted to wear trendy jeans and shorts like everyone else, so when I was fourteen, I got a part-time job at a donut shop to earn money to buy my own clothes. Every weekend for a year, my mom got up super early to drive me there and picked me up after work. I made $2 an hour plus tips serving coffee and donuts, which they let me help make. It was a sweet gig in more ways than one.

As my parents spent a lot of time volunteering at the church, I became a volunteer too. When I was fourteen, the parish priest asked my parents if I could join him on the annual ski trip to Aspen, Colorado. It was a coveted invitation, and it was mostly the kids or the kids of parents that helped out a lot at the school or church who got invited. Ten days skiing and food would be covered, we only had to pay for half of the plane ticket. I was excited to be going. But the thrill soon turned to disappointment when the priest started making inappropriate overtures to us girls. He would grab our butts and make us kiss him on the lips and sit us on his lap. He had a key to every room and would enter without knocking, trying to catch us changing our clothes. Several times he laid on top of me in my bed. I got so scared I wanted to go home, but my mom and dad had never traveled and didn't know how to arrange it. Thankfully, the older girls knew how to handle him and coached the rest of us in the best ways to avoid him. When I got home, I tried to tell my parents and other adults what had happened, but nobody seemed to want to listen. I think they knew it was true, but didn't know how to deal with it, and didn't want to believe it. They just wanted it to go away. So, I stopped talking about it after that.

Nineteen years later, Father William Brennan was "retired from office"—the eighteenth priest to be disciplined in the Archdiocese of Detroit in 2003 for sexual misconduct involving minors.[1]

From the time I left my job at the donut shop until I graduated from school, I worked a variety of part-time jobs. I also babysat so much that I was able to save enough to buy my mom a gift of a gold "Mother's ring" with all her kids' birthstones in it. She wore it a lot. Now that she's passed, it's come back to me.

When I was seventeen, I got a job at a doctor's office. However, when I learned that the success of the medical practice was founded on the unethical (but highly profitable) business of over-prescribing diet and pain medications, my illusions about the "care" industry started to crumble.

I was surprised when my boyfriend's grandma showed up one day for a refill of her "diet" meds. When I took a peek at her medical notes, I couldn't believe what I read. She'd been a patient there for 20 years. Throughout that entire period, she had regularly been prescribed amphetamines—i.e., speed—for weight loss. That was so immoral!

Baffled that they were still prescribing amphetamines to an elderly woman who now weighed more than when she had started taking the "diet meds," I asked her doctor why he was still prescribing them. "Oh well," he said dismissively, "She likes coming here, and they make her feel so good, she's able to get a lot more done."

I got called into the manager's office more than once for questioning the doctors' decisions. But as far as I was educated, patients were not supposed to be given more than 30 days of pain meds, and yet they'd come to that practice like it was a meth house and ask for more after ten days. When I'd say no, they couldn't have them, I'd get told that wasn't my decision to make.

Since my parents didn't have a college fund for me, it was never on my agenda. I think I just knew that I had to work. I'd always been very creative growing up. I loved drawing and coloring, and when I wasn't creating things, I was taking them apart. I was fascinated by how things worked and used to enjoy watching my dad taking things apart. So, when Dad said I didn't have to go to college, I could make a good living working at the Ford assembly plant and get a good pension and retire from there, I took note. On graduating from high school, I answered an ad in the paper and joined him in the automotive industry, which, in the late 1980s, was still very much a man's world.

I started out as an engineering assistant in United Technologies Automotive division, where I handled all the paperwork for the engineers. But it wasn't long before I started feeling bored. The work wasn't challenging enough for me. I wanted to prove myself, build a good career. When I asked for something more difficult and interesting to do, however, the engineers would brush me off. "Just go sit at your desk, and we'll bring you something when we have it," they'd say.

"But I'm just sitting here doing nothing," I would protest.

They must have got tired of my constant complaining because one day, Dave P., who was in charge of the engineers I supported, set me up with a drafting board. "Here are some drafting tools, and some paper," he said. "Now, go draw this wire assembly." Of course, he didn't really think I could do it; they just wanted to shut me up. But to his shock—and mine—I drew it from merely eyeballing it.

"That's very good," Dave admitted. "It looks almost exactly like the wire harness."

After that, Dave took me under his wing and became my mentor. Dave was like a father to me. He arranged for me to attend drafting and Auto-CAD classes through a tuition reimbursement program. United Technologies then taught me their CAD program via an internal training program, and suddenly, I was working in the CAD department updating drawings for the engineers.

For a while, I was enjoying the new challenges, but once I'd mastered them, I started to lose interest again. It was becoming too dull. When I announced I didn't want to do that anymore, they decided to move me into the lab where there were about 31 guys to just two women. That's when the years of watching my dad taking things apart and emulating his tinkering started to pay off. They began letting me dismantle and rebuild computers and test and build DC motors. Dad had taught me to be careful when stripping things down and to lay the components out in a way that would enable me easily to put them back where they belonged. I was given the task of teaching the engineers the difference between Toyota's dashboard switches and those of our competitors. I'd dismantle the switches and lay the parts out side by side so they could see for themselves that Toyota's switches had superior parts. I loved tinkering, and I had a blast learning how to weld, winding armatures for DC motors, and calibrating equipment. It was so much fun.

Then some higher-ups determined that they weren't utilizing my skills enough.

"We'll send you to project management classes, and then we'll be able to make you a project manager on new car builds," Dave declared. Given that it was still mostly a man's world in that industry, I had expected some kickback from the guys. But while there was a lot of what we would today call sexist behavior, my rise through the ranks proved to be surprisingly smooth and rapid. Why that was, I'm not entirely sure, but I suspect it might have been because I cared about people, and I was always willing to help out, even if it meant side-stepping a rule or two. For example, when someone in the motor lab needed a part from the electronics lab but was told they couldn't get one because it wasn't in the motor lab's budget, I'd go get it for them. The important thing to me was to get the job done, and I loved connecting people who could be helpful to one another in that regard.

I was privileged to study Project Management under Harold Kerzner, the highly respected emeritus professor of systems management at Baldwin Wallace University and senior executive director for Project Management at the International Institute for Learning.[2] I have used the techniques and skills he taught me on virtually every project I've managed since then, including the movie project I worked on with Elvis Presley's step-brother. (Yes, you read that right! And, yes, we will get to that part of my story a bit later.)

Bill Doran was the Director of Training and Development at United Technologies, and he was determined to change the culture of the organization. I was just 24 when I was assigned to Bill to do leadership training. After my training, I spent the next few years traveling extensively between Detroit, Fort Wayne, Indiana, and Zanesville, Ohio. I trained hundreds of people, including plant managers and their staff, and even on occasion, some vice presidents and their staff.

Oh, how easily we overlook the little things that lead to significant turning points in our life! For it was one such vice president who unwittingly bumped me off the path I was treading and nudged me in a direction I never could have imagined for myself back then.

It started when I was forced into a very public disagreement in the middle of a training session with this gentleman, who was VP of the wire division. I was talking about authority and responsibility when he rudely interrupted me. "Gail, there's no difference between authority and responsibility," he admonished me in a somewhat superior tone of voice,

"Yeah, there is." I countered. "If you give me the responsibility and I don't have the authority, there's a big difference."

He was adamant. "Nope. There's no difference," he argued.

I didn't know if he was establishing his superiority because I was a woman, because I was young, or if he was provocative for the sake of it. But I knew what I knew, and I wasn't in the mood to back down. The tension was palpable. For a few moments, neither of us said anything. I wanted to run out of the room and cry. Bill Doran, who was sitting in on the class, quickly got to his feet and said, "You two need to agree to disagree."

Since I had no choice, I said no more, but my Scorpio self couldn't quite let it go. As a project manager, I understood that responsibility and authority are not the same things. If you're responsible for completing a project, but have no official authority over your team members, it can be challenging to keep them on target. You have to be a good motivator; people have to *want* to work with you. Thus, I'd learned to treat team members with respect, to get to know them as individuals, and be willing to go the extra mile for them when necessary. In return, they would want to help me meet deadlines and get projects completed within the allocated budget.

So, I decided to find somebody who could write an article on the subject of authority and responsibility differences and somehow get it in front of that vice president. I tracked down a guy online who regularly wrote about leadership for business magazines and asked him if he would write an article for me. He agreed. When it was published, I positioned the magazine on the VP's desk with the article face up and then retreated to my cubicle to await the follow-up. He didn't keep me waiting long. When he emerged from his office, demanding to know why I had put the article on his desk, I calmly reminded him of the discussion we'd had.

"Well…" He blustered, waving the magazine in the air. Then, unable to think of anything else to say, he turned on his heel and abruptly walked away, muttering, "This is exactly what I said."

Willing to be gracious in victory, I finally let the matter go. But if I thought that would be the end of it, I was wrong. That altercation proved to be the catalyst for quitting my job and moving to Texas, where I'd been offered a job at almost four times my current salary… by the same guy, Travis, who had written the article for me, who lived in Texas and was starting up a telecommunications consulting firm.

For nine years, I had enjoyed my elevation through the eleven different positions I'd held at United Technologies. My mentors and teachers had honed my talent for drawing into a technically solid skill for drafting and CAD Operation and taught me first-class Project Management and Leadership skills. All of which would ultimately be critical to the success of the most evolutionary project I would ever undertake.

But that was still a long way off. I was grateful for the teachers, the opportunities, and the generous tuition reimbursement program that had funded my studies almost all the way to a bachelor's degree. But I was eager to leave Michigan and see what awaited me in the wider world beyond.

CHAPTER TWO

Culture Shock!

It was 1997, I was 27 years old and filled with a giddy mix of trepidation and excitement to be embarking on the next phase of my life. But while the next chapter proved to be undeniably instructive, all did not turn out quite as I had naively anticipated before I left Detroit, Michigan.

To be clear, I did not harbor any romantic inclinations toward my new "boss," Travis, before I moved to Texas. I knew he was married, I had met his wife on a previous visit. And he had mentioned having two children from an earlier marriage who lived in Houston and came to visit him one weekend a month. But none of that concerned me. After all, I had come to Texas for the job opportunity, and to get out of Detroit. As John Lennon once claimed, however, "life is what happens to you when you're busy making other plans." And as I would eventually discover, life definitely had a plan for me—as I believe it does for all of us.

Over the years, I've learned that influential teachers rarely announce themselves as such. It takes hindsight to appreciate and acknowledge the impact they had on our lives. That was true of Travis.

But I'm getting ahead of myself.

As I was quitting my job, selling my house in Michigan, and preparing to relocate to Texas, I had no idea that my new boss would turn out to be my first spiritual teacher. Or that the temporary residence I was taking up in the house he shared with his wife would turn into something different.

Travis and I soon eased into a good working relationship. My technical knowledge and project management skills quickly proved to be an asset to his consulting business, which, to our surprise, rapidly grew into an international enterprise. In July of 1998, after a series of meetings, which Travis and I had frequently attended as consultants, our client, GTE, completed its merger with Bell Atlantic and became Verizon Communications. And our little company just happened to have the great good fortune to be right in the middle of that merger at a time that was to become notorious for dot com explosions.

On the domestic side, however, the situation at home between Travis, his wife, and me, gradually got more complicated. It soon became apparent that Travis wanted our partnership to expand beyond business to encompass every facet of our lives. And since Travis's wife didn't seem to object to the attention Travis was paying to me, he and I slowly slid into an open but still adulterous relationship. Soon after, Travis's wife decided to up and leave, clearing the path for Travis and me to eventually marry.

In retrospect, I cannot say if I was in love with Travis or just totally enamored with him. He struck me as a man who was sophisticated, educated, and afraid of nothing, and he embodied so many things that I had never encountered before. Growing up in Michigan, I had never met anyone who wore cowboy boots, but being tall and confident, Travis carried them off with panache. The fact that he was sixteen years older than me and already had a successful career as a NASA scientist behind him convinced me that he must be a genius. And then there were his piercing blue eyes, which seemed to see right through you. The things that excited me the most, however, were Travis' experience and wisdom, and the fact that he was willing to hand me the keys to everything he knew… and not just about business either. Travis opened up a world that was in direct contrast to the one in which I'd been raised. I felt like Audrey Hepburn in the movie "My Fair Lady" in which Professor Higgins transforms the know-nothing urchin Eliza Doolittle into a grand lady. Travis was sophisticated and worldly. He taught me proper grammar and manners; that people don't eat off paper plates, and that you have a salad fork, a dessert spoon, and a butter knife… things I'd never known.

We traveled the world, visiting Switzerland, Egypt, Indonesia, Malaysia, and Peru. And he opened my eyes to spirituality, consciousness, and metaphysics. He introduced me to books by Carlos Castaneda and Buckminster Fuller, and suddenly I was reading everything I could get my hands on. I learned about quantum physics, shamanism, energy, alternative healing, the glorious, multidimensional nature of life, the magic of the universe, source… and so much more. It was like a dam had burst its banks, and I was swept along on an ocean of new discoveries. I wanted to know everything. "Why are some people happy and others sad?" "Why do some people get sick while others who are exposed to the same things don't?" *Why this…? Why that..? Why everything…?*

For the first time in my life, I became an avid student, an excited participant, and a believer in the miraculous. And I felt truly blessed. Like King Midas, everything we touched seemed to turn to gold. Our business boomed. I was debt-free before the age of 30. I was billing my consultancy services at $250 an hour, we had paid off the house, and I had bought myself a brand new Toyota 4-Runner—*with cash!* Life was exciting. We traveled all over the world for business, for pleasure, for my education, for spiritual experiences… and nothing, no place, no expense, no experience, or spiritual quest seemed beyond us.

After being molested by the Catholic priest at fourteen, I had turned my back on religion and God. I was learning about Buddhism, Hinduism, Shamanism, and it all made sense to me. All we have to do is live in this higher vibration of love and acceptance, just be a good person, no hell and damnation, and all that. It felt so refreshing. Whenever I had a migraine, an asthma attack, or any bodily pain, Travis only had to place his hands on me, and I would feel better. *How does he do that?* I'd marvel, convinced that he must have some secret knowledge or superhuman healing power. The doors to learning had been flung wide open. And like a child who is suddenly turned loose in an overstocked candy store after a lifetime of eating only bland and tasteless vegetables, I greedily soaked it all up.

But it wasn't all light and love.

Every month or so, Travis would fly his children in from Houston to spend the weekend with us. Ethan was eleven, Grace was fourteen, and I loved having them visit. We'd pick them up at the airport, and I'd plan all sorts of entertainment and activities for us all to do together. But once we got home, Travis would go off somewhere and just leave the kids and me to do things on our own. I'd take them roller skating and to the movies. I'd play football with Ethan and take Grace shopping when she wanted to do girlie things and didn't want her brother along. Of course, they noticed that their dad was frequently missing from the activities, and would ask, "Why isn't Dad doing anything with us?" All I could say was, "Ask him." But my heart would bleed for them.

As time went on, I learned that there was another side to Travis… a side that was capable of doing some very bizarre things… like putting a gun to his head and saying he wanted me to watch him blow his brains out. The first time I got to see that side of him, I was so shocked and upset, I tried to run out the front door. I almost had it open, but he slammed it shut, yelling, "Just watch! Just watch me kill myself." Terrified, I just crawled into a corner and lay curled up in the fetal position, crying like I'd never cried in my life before.

The children, who apparently had seen it all before, were not impressed with their father's behavior. "I don't know how you put up with him,"

Grace would say. In truth, I was beginning to wonder about that myself. Apparently, Travis had neglected to tell me that he was bi-polar. I found out from his mother when she said that he refused to take any meds. While it did explain some of his actions, it certainly didn't excuse them. As Travis's behavior became more erratic, the addictive part of his personality emerged. He was addicted to sex and food. He'd eat and eat until he'd put on around a hundred pounds, and then he'd diet like crazy to lose it. He wanted sex all the time and openly claimed that he was entitled to have more than one wife at the same time to satisfy his sexual appetites. I didn't know how to handle any of it. I was entirely out of my depth. I felt disillusioned, nervous, and incapable of reconciling the out-of-control, addiction-crazed Travis with the man who had awakened my slumbering spirit and opened my mind to more enlightened ways of thinking.

The more successful our business became, the more time we spent apart. We had contracts with companies in Egypt. As I became more involved with managing the Verizon contract in Texas, he started spending more time in Egypt, where I suspected he was having an affair with one of the girls at the company there. I noticed that when we spoke on the phone, he seemed preoccupied and distant. "Okay, well, I love you," I would say toward the end of a call, more to test where his head was at than anything else.

"Err… um…Yeah, me too!" He'd respond unconvincingly.

And the more erratic and uninterested Travis grew, the more worried and stressed I became. Trying to figure out what might be going on was exhausting. My health started to suffer. I was having more migraines and had some reproductive issues starting. I couldn't relax during the day, and I couldn't sleep at night. The constant strain and uncertainty triggered my health problems. I felt so edgy and nervous all the time, it was making me ill, and I knew that I had to confront Travis. "Why don't you just say 'I love you' back to me?" I burst out at the end of a call. "I know you're with someone else right now. So why don't you just admit it." But he wouldn't. When he hung up, I was so upset I couldn't stop crying. Unfortunately, Travis's eleven-year-old son Ethan was in the house at the time and had heard everything and was almost as distraught as I was. "Is there anything I can do?" He kept patting me on the back and asking.

"No," I sobbed, knowing that there was nothing anyone could do. It was just a matter of time.

Things began rapidly to disintegrate after that. The next time he had one of his "suicidal" episodes, I told him, "Just go ahead and do it already because I can't do this anymore."

When the end finally came, we were in Peru where we had planned to take part in a shamanic journey.

Travis had gone to Peru a week ahead of me. I had barely arrived to join him when he confessed that he had fallen madly in love with our assistant tour guide (who I shall call Cora) and said he wanted a divorce. By that time, I was so wrung out emotionally, I couldn't even feel unhappy. All I could say was, "Why did you make me come all the way to Peru to ask me for a divorce when you could have told me before I left?"

I considered my options. One of the highlights we'd planned for our trip was an Ayahuasca experience. But our tour guide decided I wasn't in the right state emotionally to participate in that. And Travis had moved into Cora's room. I could stay in Peru, where we had cold showers and no cellphone capability, or I could return home early. But I still hadn't seen Machu Picchu and Cusco. So, deciding that there had to be something I could learn from this, I made up my mind to stay and finish the trip.

I spent nine days watching Travis and Cora's relationship develop, which was undeniably humiliating and uncomfortable. At the same time, however, there were aspects of the situation that seemed so surreal, they were almost comical. I wasn't sure who was chasing whom, but I suspected this might not be the first time Cora had "fallen in love with" one of the wealthy tourists. So, I decided to use my time in Peru to do some investigating.

Meantime, as Travis didn't speak Spanish and Cora didn't speak English, and I had taken three semesters in the language, I let him rope me in as their interpreter. I played the go-between, and I let her know how much he loved her. Naturally, I took full advantage of the situation.

"Travis wants you to know that he loves you, Cora," I'd tell her, before slyly adding, "You do know that he's going to be *el jefe* (the boss) don't you?"

"No. No." She would exclaim in Spanish. "*I* am *el jefe!*"

"Well, good luck with that," I'd smirk, knowing full well that Travis was nothing if not a power trip kind of guy.

By the time we returned home, I had managed to connect with some government officials in Peru. They confirmed reports of Cora's "friendly overtures" to other American male tourists.

"Oh, no, not my Cora." Travis protested when I broke the news to him. "Hmmm. Same name, same birthday, same everything. Yep. It's definitely your Cora," I assured him. "No. No. It's not her." Travis insisted, refusing to be deterred from pursuing his new relationship.

Several weeks later, while I was still looking for a place to live so I could move out, Travis woke up one morning and said, "I think I've made a terrible mistake. I want you back." But it was too late.

My only regret was leaving Travis' children, with whom I had grown close over the years. "We hate our dad," Travis's daughter cried when I broke the news to them about our divorcing. I felt so helpless, but there was nothing I could say other than "You can't hate your dad. He's your father," and promise that we would stay in touch and still see one another. Which we have done.

When I left, Travis wouldn't let me take anything other than my clothes and car. I didn't take the Waterford Crystal he'd bought me for my birthday or the artwork he'd given me on our anniversaries. And, perhaps dumbest of all, I did not take my share of the equity in the house. Why? Maybe I still felt a degree of inferiority. For, stupidly, I let him convince me I owed everything to him. And because I was so much younger than him, and thus could start over again, I owed it to him to leave everything. My attorney was appalled. "At least take your share of the equity," he pleaded. But by that point, I'd had enough. I didn't care anymore. I had learned that life was about more than money and possessions, and I just wanted out.

So, Travis got his divorce, and everything else he wanted, including Cora, whom he married shortly after… and then divorced some years later. (One day, several years later, I received a communication from Travis. He couldn't stop himself from asking if I missed him, to which I responded, "It's been twelve years, what do *you* think?")

I had learned a great deal from Travis, for which I shall always be grateful, but I paid a high price for the lessons in terms of my health and sanity. The stress had wreaked havoc on my nervous system. The cystic acne of my youth had returned. The migraines had increased. My hair was falling out. To top it all, I was bleeding heavily during my monthly cycles, and my gynecologist was talking about a hysterectomy. I was just thirty years old and some days I felt closer to fifty.

But, oh, the relief and joy I felt at finally having the freedom to just take care of me again!

CHAPTER THREE

All Shook Up –
The King of Rock and Roll…
and ME

When I was around fifteen, my father suddenly announced that he wasn't going to attend church anymore. "Confession is silly," he declared. "Why would anyone want to confess their sins to another human being who has sins of their own to confess?" He never explained what was behind his decision, only that he didn't want to be a hypocrite. Adding, "And besides, you can pray to God without having to go to church." While I was surprised, I didn't disapprove. After the incident with our priest, I was too angry and disappointed to want anything to do with God and religion any more.

Later on, when Travis introduced me to Hinduism, Buddhism, Shamanism, and spirituality, I thought I had found a truer path. But as time passed, I started to question that too. I couldn't understand why so much hate and hypocrisy existed in the world. People were lying, cheating, and stepping on one another while professing to be "Christian" or in some way, "enlightened." I'd experienced it twice now. First, with a priest who was supposed to be God's representative on earth. Then with a man who claimed to be deeply "spiritual," but acted like he had a God-given right to possess any woman he wanted. By the time I left Travis, I was thoroughly perplexed. The spiritual path I'd started exploring had felt right to me. The books I had read, and the courses I had studied had answered a lot of questions that Catholicism had not touched. But still, I couldn't quite reconcile my intuitive spiritual leanings with the bald facts of my experience.

Since I had other priorities right then, I decided to put my spiritual explorations on the back burner while I set about rebuilding my life and health. I could take time to think about what I wanted to do next, while exploring natural ways to resolve my health issues, which I had come to believe had an emotional connection.

I remained in Texas, but moved to another city, where I bought a house, and started a consulting company called Collective Minds. Slowly, I began to rebuild my life again. I made friends and gained clients, but I still couldn't quite get a handle on the health stuff. *That's because you're still angry,* a little voice kept whispering in my head. It was true. I was angry at Travis for all the ways I felt he had lied to me, controlled me, and put me down. And I was angry at myself for all the ways that I had allowed that to happen.

As part of my self-healing program, I was determined to start digging deeper to learn more about the inner workings of the mind, the emotions, and the body, and the effects they had on each other. I expanded my reading to encompass books on the psychology of human nature. I was curious to learn more about what makes people tick, why we think and behave the way we do. I wanted to understand Travis' bizarre behavior and why I had been so willing to put up with it for so long. I followed that trail into the worlds of alternative health and medicine. Researching the mind-body connection, I discovered that our emotions and thought patterns can contribute to imbalances within the body.

I learned that the beliefs you hold about yourself and the world, and your emotions, memories, and habits can all influence your mental and physical health. I started exploring and experimenting with natural healing modalities and approaches. Reviewing my life and relationships, I saw that I had a lot of self-esteem issues. I remembered how, back when I'd first started dating, I'd attracted a lot of narcissists and men with drinking issues. I learned that's not uncommon in adult children of alcoholics. And I added every aha! of comprehension to a growing list of unhealthy patterns and behaviors that I needed to work on. Still, understanding the roots of one's patterns and emotions isn't always enough on its own to resolve things. Sometimes we need to find a way to move the stuck energy through and out of the physical body to fully discharge it. And *that,* I became aware, was precisely what I needed to do with the unhealthy, smoldering anger that still lurked beneath the surface of my smiling personality. I was still mad at Travis and myself, and no amount of understanding or relief or joy at having extricated myself from a marriage that had gone so badly wrong seemed sufficient to fully release that amount of pent-up anger. It was time to get physical.

I was at lunch with a friend at a strip mall when a sign in the window of a Karate School caught my eye. It was advertising self-defense classes for women. Instantly, something inside me went *Bingo!*

Three times a week, for the next three years, I trained in Kenpo Karate. I sparred, kickboxed, and took classes in stickfighting. It was a great place to work out. We had a lot of laughs and fun, and I loved every minute of it. And because I'm not very coordinated, one of the instructors took me under his wing and privately taught me Karate forms and sparring. I met Edmund Parker Junior, whose father Ed Parker, Sr. had trained Elvis Presley. It was Ed Jr. who taught me to have great respect for the black belts. The first time I was told to bow before a Black Belt, I thought *hell, no! Why should I bow to anyone?* But when Edmund explained how much discipline and dedication it took to achieve that coveted status, I got it. It was a humbling experience.

I remember once hearing, "How long does it take the average person to get a black belt?" To which the answer is: "The *average* person does not get a black belt."

One day, the Sifu (karate master) announced that they had invited the motivational speaker and author, David E. Stanley, to host a seminar for us. David Stanley was Elvis Presley's step-brother. I was utterly taken aback. *Elvis Presley! All right!* I thought. I mean, who hadn't heard of Elvis? He was such an icon! For the first time in a long time, I felt a flicker of excitement. Even so, it never occurred to me that attending that seminar would lead me to the next major fork in my road. Or that David E. Stanley, and to a lesser degree, Elvis Presley, would turn out to be such influential figures in the next phase of my education.

I confess that, initially, I didn't feel the same degree of connection to David that he clearly felt for me. So, when he asked me out on a date after the seminar, my ambivalence must have been apparent to him in my hesitant, "Well… okay then." But it didn't take him long to win me over.

Like Travis before him, David thought my project management skills and business acumen would be an asset in helping him build his business. Since I happened to be in the market for a new challenge, I felt that it had to be synchronicity, or at the very least, a happy coincidence.

And so it was that in early 2002, after having turned my back on Catholicism and God, and taken a moratorium on spirituality until I could find a way to separate Travis' spiritual interests and beliefs from his decidedly unspiritual behavior, I found myself loving and working with a committed *evangelist*!

The irony was not lost on me: clearly, I still had more to learn about religion, the nature of "God," and the inconsistencies between what people preach and how they behave.

David Stanley's mother, Dee, had married Elvis Presley's father, Vernon, and moved her children into Graceland when David was just four years old.

David was the youngest of Dee's three boys, and far too young to know anything about fame or stardom. To him, Elvis Presley was like a superhero. He had welcomed the boys as little brothers, showering them with toys like Santa Claus on steroids, and establishing from day one his influence as a father figure and mentor.

"When I started school, I didn't have any identity—I was just Elvis's step-brother. Elvis would come to watch me play football, but then nobody watched the game. They were all watching him instead." David later shared in an interview.[3] It wasn't until he grew up that David realized that growing up at Graceland as a member of Elvis's household and family had its darker side.

When David was sixteen, Elvis took him out of school to go on the road with him. With over 1,100 concerts in five years, touring with Elvis as first his personal aide and then his bodyguard, David was exposed to things that few adolescents get to experience. Soon, the hedonistic rock 'n roll lifestyle of private jets, easy girls, and even easier drugs (not to mention unlimited access to virtually everything else a young man could have wanted) was "just a normal way of life" for David. Unsurprisingly, it wasn't long before he, too, was fighting substance abuse issues. When Elvis's drug use slowly descended from a moderate level of medication to massive drug addiction, David grew increasingly scared and worried about his and Elvis's well-being.

When Elvis died, alone in his bathroom on August 16th, 1977, David was one of the first people on the scene. Shocked and devastated, but not entirely surprised, David saw Elvis's death as a dire warning.

"Elvis's death was my resurrection." He wrote, years later in his book *My Brother Elvis: The Final Years,* which was published in 2016. "His passing was my wakeup call to my road to redemption. I mean, when I walked into Elvis's bathroom along with several other guys, and they rolled him over, and we cradled him in our arms and saw that sight of a guy that we loved and adored—and specifically me—it had a profound impact on my life. [I thought] 'I'm next.' And I saw first-hand what drugs could do. I saw what abuse can do with medication. And I realized if I don't clean it up pretty quick myself, I'm next."

With Elvis gone and Vernon's announcement that everyone was out of a job, David knew he had to clean up his act and find a way to support himself. With just a 9th grade education, a drug addiction problem, and few skills other than those he had learned as a bodyguard and aide to Elvis, it wasn't easy. But Elvis's death had galvanized David into action, motivating him to kick the drugs and use his experience and knowledge to help others.

People who knew Elvis claimed they'd never met anyone who exuded such an innate sense of confidence and power as he did. But watching David on stage that first time, I couldn't help thinking that Elvis's secrets about stage presence and magnetism had clearly rubbed off on his step-brother. I'd heard the phrase: "owning the room." But I had never witnessed anyone actually doing it until that evening. And I was awed by the ease with which David held his audience in the palm of his hand.

In the beginning, I think I was more infatuated with David than in love with him (that came later). Just like Travis, he was confident, worldly, and sixteen years older than me. But as I watched how David handled himself with people, patiently relaying the same story he'd told over and over again to others, I realized how fortunate I was to know this guy who was so willing to share his time and experiences with people. David made people happy, and it was uplifting for me to witness the joy he brought to others when he gave them glimpses of his life with Elvis. I wanted to bring some of that to the elderly men and women at the assisted living center where I volunteered. When David agreed to come to talk to them, all the residents were so excited. We made lots of copies of pictures of David and Elvis together, which he signed for all the residents. And when the residents shared the news with their families, their kids and grandkids all turned up too. David was his usual charismatic self, and I was fascinated to watch his audience, which encompassed both the young and the not-so-young, hanging on his every word. It was so cool. I really admired the grace and ease with which he did that and quietly wished that I could cultivate that same ability to lift people's spirits.

Without being too pushy, David let me know that he would like to bring me back to God. He gently pointed out how the stories I'd been telling myself to justify my rejection of religion were irrational. Now that I was older and wiser, and understood how reactionary fourteen-year-olds can be, I could see the logic in his reasoning. So, I agreed to take another look at the Bible.

Even so, my left-brained, scientifically-oriented mind didn't cease questioning. *If we cannot determine the accuracy of events that occurred just 20 or 30 years ago, how can we be sure that events we read about in our Bibles aren't misinterpretations? Or even deliberate distortions? After all, it's often claimed that not all of what we read in our history books is necessarily true.* Since history is generally written by those who won the battles, the "facts" are bound to get skewed in the retelling. In light of this, I thought it naïve to base one's beliefs and faith on what almost certainly is a biased perception of events. However, whenever I would say this to David, he would just look at me blankly and declare, "If it's in the Bible, it must be true." And that would be the end of the discussion. We never really argued about religion. David loved me and accepted me for who I was. He simply continued to follow his own beliefs and allowed me the room to determine my own understandings by immersing myself in books by Wayne Dyer, Neale Donald Walsch, Edgar Cayce, and a host of other popular writers and spiritual teachers.

David had a charismatic personality. Everyone who met him seemed to fall under his spell. And it wasn't just because he was Elvis' step-brother. David didn't need a script or notes; he was an extemporaneous performer, self-assured, with a hypnotic voice and manner of speaking and considerable presence. People literally hung on his every word. He was persuasive and charming. And he had such a trustworthy manner that people lined up to talk to him and follow him. They even gave him money to invest in his ideas for movies, books, or anything he presented.

And in the seven years that we were together, I saw him use every one of those qualities to his advantage.

I didn't know why I should think Evangelists would be any less hypocritical than some of the religious people I'd grown up around. Still, I was as shocked when David confided that he'd "met more crooks and thieves in evangelism than he ever met in rock and roll," as I had been by Father Brennan's behavior or some of the allegedly spiritual people I'd met through Travis.

David was a popular motivational speaker, and he traveled the country, presenting talks and seminars on how to overcome obstacles and follow your dreams. I went with him. I took care of all the admin work and assisted David in developing his motivational talks. I helped him with his speaker kits and event planning. And I pitched organizations to get him booked as a speaker. Life on the road wasn't always easy; David could be quite controlling sometimes and didn't like being told what to do. He didn't like being reminded that, just like any business, we had to create budgets and stick to them. Having spent many years with Elvis, who wasn't known for his frugality, David didn't understand why we couldn't follow Elvis's model of overspending and then paying for it with another sell-out tour.

We had a few knock-down-drag-out fights over that. But in between those, we had a lot of fun together.

One day, I asked him, "So what's *your* dream?"

"Well, when Elvis is your big brother, your father figure, your friend and mentor, how do you do something bigger and better than him?"

"Well, there's got to be something Elvis couldn't do," I countered.

"Nope," David shook his head adamantly. "Elvis could do *anything*. He could walk into the President of the United States' office and just go rummaging through his drawers for souvenirs. He could go to any city and ask for a police badge, and they would give it to him just because he was Elvis."

"Oh, come on," I insisted. "There has to be *something*." Something in my voice must have triggered David because this time, instead of immediately dismissing the conversation, he paused for several moments before slowly drawling, "You know… Elvis did always want to direct a movie. But his manager, Colonel Parker, would never let him. 'You're an actor. You're a singer. That's it,' he'd say."

I smiled as an idea took hold. "Well, then," I announced as if it was a done deal. "It looks like you're going to direct a movie!"

"What?!" David looked at me as if I was crazy. "Have you ever made a movie?"

"No. But how hard can it be?" I shot back at him.

It was the stupidest thing I ever said. But it catapulted David and me on a seven-year journey during which, without any experience to guide us, we transformed ourselves into Hollywood film producers.

The first three years of trying to get the movie made were fun, the last four years not so much. I helped David raise all the money for the project, which was an eye-opening experience in that it exposed some of the differences between us. I didn't want to take money from people that could not afford to lose it. Not being quite so sensitive, David was happy to accept money from anyone.

Since I had a business background, I wrote the first business plan. I filled out all the paperwork for investors, directed the next steps in the process, and project managed the entire plan. David was the face of the company. We took a two-day film school course from Dov Simens, and we traveled all over the United States. I organized presentations and meetings with private investors. I learned the difference between accredited and unaccredited investors, and filing in compliance with the Blue Sky laws, which is necessary when you take money from out-of-state investors, and are operating under a Private Placement Memorandum. Eventually, we raised our entire budget to shoot the film, *Protecting the King*, which was about a sixteen-year-old boy named David who went to work for his world-famous stepbrother, Elvis, and protected him from ultimately everything but himself.[4]

We learned fast. And we had a blast doing it. There were so many fun things that happened during the making of that movie. We cast some well-known actors, including Tom Sizemore, who were great fun to work with. But it wasn't all smooth sailing. We had to face several roadblocks that we hadn't envisioned. We weren't allowed to use actual footage of Elvis. We wanted to film in Utah, we had put money down on a hotel, but then it got returned to us along with a message saying that we couldn't shoot there. We later learned that the hotel was in some way related to the Scientology community and wondered whether The Presley Estate had put a stop to it because the movie wasn't going to show Elvis in the best light. We were never able to prove that. Still, it is feasible, given that *Protecting the King* was going to be a behind-the-scenes movie that portrayed the real sex, drugs, and rock and roll Elvis, who wanted to kill Priscilla's boyfriend, as opposed to the upstanding citizen, apple pie kind of guy that everyone believed him to be. It's a hard, raw movie, with a lot of F-words in it, and we had to get errors and omissions insurance to show that it portrayed a true and accurate depiction of what it was like to be on the road with Elvis Presley.

David, as mentioned earlier, had learned how to spend money Elvis Presley-style. But he wasn't Elvis. And he hadn't learned how to make money to Elvis's standard. So, when things got rough financially, I'd keep the money flowing by self-directing my IRA funds and my life savings into the film's business account. I sold all my stocks, all my gold, and ran through my entire savings account in the process.

David and I fought a lot over relationship issues as well as business issues. It's a miracle we completed the film. Dealing with all the logistics of movie production with its inevitable problems and screw-ups was easy, thanks to the project management skills and experience I'd gathered over the years. Dealing with some of the people and the issues created by their big egos and insecurities and low morals was, on the other hand, hugely challenging and exhausting.

I quickly discovered that there were a lot of repulsive people in Hollywood, and I don't mean physically. They would say things to me, like

"What gives you the right to be executive producer of this movie when I've been doing this for 28 years?" Or "I paid my dues; I've worked on commercials, I've done porn, what have you done to earn this position?"

I was shocked at the lengths some people would go to secure a job or a role in the movie. And I was disappointed and appalled by the unprofessionalism, and the predatory behavior of some of the industry guys David had hired, who seemed more interested in seeing if they could use their position to get laid by someone auditioning for a part, than in producing a great movie. They didn't like me because I wasn't afraid to stand up to them or call them out on their behavior. I was known as the set "Bitch."

When we were casting, the guys who were interviewing would look at me and say, "Put her on the 'yes' list" or "Put her on the 'no' list." There was one day when we auditioned a girl who clearly wanted a part so badly, she had no scruples. I was sitting next to David. But she completely ignored me as she gave him a long, lingering, wide-eyed look and emphatically announced, "I would do *anything* for this part." All the crew knew that David and I were dating, but that didn't stop them from smirking at me and saying, "Put her on the 'yes' list." *To hell with that!* I thought, defiantly scratching her name on the 'no' list.

It wasn't all bad. I met some lovely people along the way. And there were times when I was so outraged and shocked by the insanity of the business, I just wanted to quit. But I had made a commitment to our investors, some of whom were good friends by then, and my parents, too, and I refused to let them down. So, we finished the movie, did the film festivals in Germany, walked the red carpet in France, got a distribution deal, and that was it... mission completed. Or, so we thought.

It was the distribution deal that let us down. After seven years in the movie industry, David felt he knew enough to negotiate a contract without the help of an attorney. He was wrong. Although the movie sold in over eighteen countries, we never received any return on the investment. Elvis's hardcore fans didn't really care for it, because they only wanted to see him in a positive light. Elvis was the King, a god to them, and they didn't want to see his imperfections. But as gifted as he was, Elvis Presley was a human being; just like the rest of us, he had a shadow side. The truth was that the darker aspects of Elvis portrayed in the movie only told a small part of the story. As David said to me, "He was the nicest guy you ever met, and he was the meanest guy you ever met. But even so, there are some stories about Elvis that I will take to my grave."

After having met some of the "good ol' boy" network of people that worked for Elvis (widely known as the Memphis Mafia), and sitting around the table with individuals like Lamar Fike and Sonny West, I understood why. More than 30 years had passed, and with them, many members of the Memphis Mafia. But still, when those guys got together, it was like Elvis had only died yesterday, and those that were left were still in "protect the King" mode. Protecting Elvis was what defined them. I found that so sad. As David once confided to me, "I don't know who likes me because I am Elvis's stepbrother or David Stanley."

It's hard to imagine what it must be like to live with that level of fame. Even today, on August 16th, "the day that Elvis died" is still marked by vigils in England and other countries across the world. That's remarkable considering Elvis never toured outside the USA, so he never visited any of those places (not because he didn't want to, but because Colonel Parker was not a US citizen, and did not have a passport). It blows my mind that people still sob and weep as if it has just happened. I often wonder: *what type of person was Elvis Presley really*? Not what sort of character or personality, but what kind of *being* was he that he possessed such tremendous energy?

After the movie was over, I felt like Anne Hathaway's character when she quit her job at the end of *The Devil Wears Prada* and threw her cell phone into the fountain. *Done!*

Making the movie with David was undoubtedly the hardest thing I had ever done. It had been such a massive undertaking; some of those times were fabulous, and some of them were so manic I just wanted to throw in the towel. But we got it done, and by the time it was over, David and I came to an amicable agreement that we were done too. There was no shaming and blaming. We had taken on a colossal task together, and we had seen it through to the end. And now it was time for us both to move on. I had been feeling a growing restlessness for some time, an uneasy sense that something important was missing from my life, but I couldn't fathom what. It had never been about fame or money for me, I knew that much. I was motivated more by accomplishing what people claimed could not be done by two amateurs. And I was especially excited by the thought of doing something that could change the world. Although I had no clue what that might be, something told me that I wouldn't ever be truly happy if I didn't allow myself to find out.

David and I parted without the animosity that had accompanied my divorce from Travis, and I took the now-familiar route of taking time out to consider my options. I took stock of how I had acquitted myself on the journey that David and I had undertaken together, and what I had gained and lost. I felt immensely grateful for all the positive things I had learned from him, and the confidence I'd won, both professionally and personally. Taking on the role of film producer had challenged and raised my project management skills to a whole new level. I had been instrumental in raising and spending millions of dollars without going over budget on a feature film. I'd paced myself through sixteen extremely intense days of filming, with 120 people on set, making sure that everyone from the stars to the crew was happy and had whatever they needed to do their job. I'd smoothed over problems created by arrogant a-holes, who carelessly treated less essential members of the crew like crap, and kept some of those same people from quitting the job they badly needed by showing them how much we appreciated and valued their contribution to the project. I'd entered the cutthroat world of Hollywood as a know-nothing novice, and stood my ground with the best and the worst of them, and won respect. I'd learned from David how to own a room and how to take control of difficult situations, as well as how not to use status, position, or celebrity to manipulate or take advantage of people. And I'd learned to end a relationship with dignity, kindness, and compassion for our human failings.

David and I didn't stay together as partners, but our care for one another endures. I call him up to check on him every so often, and he does the same for me. And I still say "I love you" at the end of our conversations, not in a romantic way, but for all we had been through together.

After weighing it all up, there were only two downsides. One, having depleted my savings and retirement funds, I was now broke. And two, I'd been so focused on taking care of everyone else's needs, I had overlooked one fundamental principle. Taking care of others is best served by filling your own cup first.

Once again, my body was reminding me that I had been neglecting my health.

CHAPTER FOUR

The Impossible Dream

Only someone who has suffered a migraine headache truly understands how debilitating they can be. According to the Migraine Research Foundation, migraine is the third most prevalent illness in the world, affecting 39 million men, women, and children in the U.S. and one billion worldwide. This painful neurological condition can assault all the senses—the intense head pain and extreme sensitivity to lights, sounds, and smells… nausea, and vomiting… the complete loss of functionality… trust me, there are few things more incapacitating than a full-on migraine attack. [5]

When I'd met David, I thought I had done everything humanly possible to release the stranglehold migraine had had on my life for twenty-three years. Attacks came on at the stupidest moments. I'd be shopping at the grocery store and suddenly start losing my vision. I would have to abandon the grocery cart and leave, knowing that in 45 minutes, I would be incapable of functioning. I'd drive home with little peripheral vision, praying that I'd make it back without causing a traffic accident. I'd tried acupuncture and chiropractic. I'd tried yoga, and had been to past life regressors, but nothing had come close to reducing their severity, let alone cured them. So, to imagine that I might one day have reason to be grateful to migraines for setting my life on a whole new trajectory seemed an utter impossibility.

However, soon after we had committed to making the Elvis movie, I'd introduced David to a conference for entrepreneurs on raising capital, protecting intellectual property, and constructing a business plan. This was the kind of event where c-levels could network with other executives willing to share their knowledge and experience, so I immediately registered us to attend. I knew the founder, and I was convinced David would find his way to the platform at this event. He did. It was the platform where we raised or were introduced to investors to make our *Protecting the King* movie a reality.

One of the speakers at the event was a man who —I'll call him Fred— had designed a light box. Like David, Fred was a persuasive speaker. I listened, enthralled, as he shared a story about a little boy who'd had 27 operations before he was seven years old. According to Fred, the Mayo Clinic had told this boy's mother that her child would never talk or walk, and would never grow hair or teeth. He accompanied his story with photographs of this poor little boy whose eyes were completely blank as if there was no consciousness and no soul behind them.

When Fred first met the family, he was so touched he offered free sessions in the light box. "Nobody gets to tell me that my boy will never walk or talk or have hair," the child's mother declared as she accepted his offer. "Nobody gets to say that. I'm gonna do everything I can to make sure that he has the best quality life he can have."

When Fred showed photos of the child taken six months later, after several sessions in the light box, my jaw dropped. The intensity of life and light shining out of the boy's eyes left me speechless. All I could think was *What the heck!* I was even more stunned when the child walked onto the stage and stood beside Fred at the end of his talk. He was using arm crutches, but he was walking! And he had hair on his head and teeth! And all because of this light box?!

It seemed inconceivable, impossible even, but *Oh, my God!* I marveled. *If it can do that for him, what could it do for me and others?* Then, out of nowhere came another thought: *It would be so cool to help people in the way that little boy has been supported.*

The moment Fred finished speaking, I bullied my way up to the front of the stage, and threw the question at him: "Will this help with migraine headaches?" He looked at me, and calmly responded, "The body doesn't know disease by name."

What? I thought uncomprehending. Coming from the corporate world, it seemed like such a stupid answer. All I was looking for was a straight forward yes or no. When he didn't say any more, I turned away, shoulders slumped in disappointment.

Now, of course, I understand that you cannot guarantee to heal anyone of any physical ailment and to claim to cure migraines would be unethical and illegal. But those images of the boy and Fred's light box never left me. They stayed right where they were, sitting at the edge of my consciousness like a faded dream that has gone fuzzy around the edges, or a distant hope that never quite gets fulfilled.

It didn't help that over the next seven years while working on bringing *Protecting the King* to the big screen, I kept running into Fred at various conferences in different states. *Why does this person keep coming back into my life?* I wondered, irked by the constant reminders, not to mention the continuing migraines.

After we finished the movie in 2007, we ran into Fred again. Motivated by the possibility of getting a testimonial from Elvis's step-brother, he invited us to visit his Wellness Center in Arizona for some sessions. Since I was curious to know why Fred kept showing up, and if there was any chance the light box might be able to help my migraines, we accepted his offer.

Although the weekend experience was definitely relaxing, I couldn't honestly say that I noticed any miracles or even anything different. Until two months later, when, out on a bicycle ride, instead of stopping to catch my breath at the top of a hill, I realized I wasn't even winded.

That's when it hit me; *I hadn't had even one small episode of asthma in several weeks... and the only thing I'd done differently was the light box! No, it couldn't have been that silly light box, because it didn't do anything. Maybe I just outgrew asthma.* I told myself.

I was wrong. Twelve years later, it still hasn't returned.

The migraines, however, were a different story.

By then, I knew that David and I had to go our separate ways. Even so, it wasn't until a client flew me to Colorado for a meeting soon after our light box sessions that I found the impetus to start the unraveling process. It seemed that the light box was energetically aligning things right before my very eyes.

It sounds like a cliché, but from the moment I stepped off the plane in Denver, I felt—no, I *knew*—that I had come home. On my return to Texas, I immediately put a "for sale" sign up in front of my house and told David I was moving. He was quite shocked at this quick decision, but I knew with my entire being that it was my destiny to do this.

I found a temporary consulting job in Denver and got found in turn by a beautiful dog with whom I instantly fell in love. And while the migraines didn't disappear right away, they did reduce in intensity. *Okay,* I conceded, *maybe this light box* can *do something after all.*

In 2008, still quite broke after investing everything I had in the movie, and still plagued by migraines, a little voice in my head started urging me to go back and give the light box another try. Struggling to find more consulting work, I was aware that I was becoming increasingly stressed. After resisting for a while, I finally decided to listen to my intuition and go back for more light box sessions in Arizona. As if by magic, I noticed that my life suddenly started flowing again after the sessions. I could see a definite pattern between my sessions in the light box and the way my life was flowing—as if someone, or some *thing*, was triggering a reset button.

When I met an elderly couple in Denver who were talking about opening a center using the light box, my instantaneous reaction was *Oh, no. I wanted to do that!* I was shocked that such a radical idea was lurking in my subconscious. But the more I examined it, the more I realized that it was just plain silly. I was in no position to invest in a new business. Besides, what did I know about operating a health business?

So, I offered to help the couple raise the money to open their center instead. After working with them for several months, however, I reluctantly conceded that they were both a little too old and too fragile health-wise to be operating a wellness center. I could not, with integrity, encourage anyone to put up investment money to support the idea.

Nonetheless, the seed had been sown.

Over the next couple of years, I returned to Arizona for sessions in the light box whenever I could. It seemed that whenever I felt stuck or hit a brick wall, a session in the light box would soon get me back in the flow.

By the time 2009 rolled around, the crippling migraines that had plagued my life for years were finally becoming less frequent and intense. I'd had about twelve sessions by that point, and I still had no idea how the light box worked, but I was living proof that it did.

I scored another consulting job and was soon enjoying a six-figure income again. But I hated every minute of it. I was traveling five days a week to Ohio and felt so alone and lost. I would be sitting on packed airplanes with hundreds of people around me, and spending time with colleagues at work, and I felt more isolated and alone than I had ever felt before. When you are not on your path and your subconscious is nagging at you 24/7, there is an uneasy feeling in your bones all the time.

What happened next was like a bad country song. The one good thing in my life was my best friend, Zeus. A 150-pound Great Pyrenees, Zeus was the love of my life. A friend of mine who lived in Texas looked after him during the week, so that I did not have to kennel Zeus for the five days I worked in Ohio every week. I would fly to Texas and stay with him on weekends and whenever I could get a day off. Zeus had come to me in 2007 when a breeder had convinced me that I should get a puppy for Buddy, my twelve-year-old Husky-Malamute. She had said that as Buddy was getting older, it made sense to have Buddy train another dog to replace him when he passed on. Puppies are a lot of work, and I didn't really want to raise another. Nor did I want to think about losing my Buddy dog. But, somehow, against my greater common sense, I found myself going along with the idea.

Buddy and I went out to the breeders' place after the litter was born. I let him walk among the new puppies, who hadn't even opened their eyes yet. And then, for some unknown reason, Buddy decided to hightail it out of there. When I saw one small pup crawling toward the exit after him, I knew we had found "the one." "That's him!" I yelled. "That's the one we want to take home." For the next several weeks, Buddy and I visited Zeus often so that when it came time for him to leave his mother, he would know he was part of our family.

For fourteen months, Buddy, Zeus, and I had a good time. Then, out of the blue one day, a tumor that I hadn't known was growing on Buddy's liver suddenly burst, and Buddy started declining fast. On a May day in 2008, I left Zeus at home to take Buddy to the emergency vet. He never came home. When the vet said that if Buddy survived the surgery, which would cost around $10,000, it was unlikely he would have the same quality of life, I knew I had a hard decision to make. I wanted so badly to get a hug from my mom, but she was 1,200 miles away. I couldn't imagine life without Buddy; he had been with me through thick and thin, through my divorce from Travis and my moves from Michigan to Texas and then to Colorado. *How would I survive without him?*

I had the doctor keep Buddy comfortable until I could come to grips with losing him. The emergency clinic was very good to us; they gave us all the time we needed alone together in a sound-proofed room. I hugged Buddy for a long time and told him how much I loved him. I didn't want to cry; I wanted to be strong for him, as he had been for me during my rough times. I lay down on the floor beside him until, eventually, the vet came and gently administered the injection that would relieve him of his pain and suffering. And then the dam broke. The moment I heard the words, "He's gone," I curled up in a ball beside my best friend and howled. Buddy was almost fourteen when he passed, and no matter how many days that added up to, it still wasn't enough. I knew I had to leave the vet's eventually. Zeus was waiting for us—for me—at home, and all I could take back home with me to Zeus was Buddy's collar. It was one of the saddest days of my life.

One day in 2009, while staying with my friend in Texas, Zeus ran away. I didn't know this until my friend picked me up at the airport when I flew in for my usual visit. I thought my friend was acting oddly. Then he confessed. Zeus had been playing in his unfenced yard the day before and had suddenly run off with another dog. I couldn't believe that he had let 24 hours go by before telling me. He said he'd spent the entire time searching for Zeus. That didn't make me feel any better. We searched for weeks. We had flyers printed with a reward for any news and pasted them all around the area. We received lots of calls, but none led us to Zeus. Eventually, I had to go back to work. When my friend called to say that he'd had a good lead—someone had described seeing a dog that looked just like Zeus, I didn't think twice about hopping on a plane to Texas. I'd lost Buddy, and I couldn't bear the thought of losing Zeus too. Unfortunately, my boss wasn't very sympathetic. I'd lost my dog. And trying to find him cost me my job. They told me if I left the job site, I would be fired, but I left anyway. Now, what was I going to do? My bad country song was taking me down and down into the blues.

I spent months looking for another job. I submitted dozens of resumes and went on lots of interviews, but, weirdly, for the first time in my life, all the doors seemed closed to me. I couldn't understand why no one seemed to be interested in employing someone with my level of skills and experience. I felt demoralized and ashamed. I had been a superstar in the automotive industry, I had built a successful international consulting firm in the telecommunications industry, and I was an executive producer in Hollywood. I was used to succeeding. That was my identity.

At least, that's what I thought.

But somewhere deep inside me, another voice was trying to get my attention. "That's not who you are," it kept taunting me in the middle of the night when I couldn't sleep. "There's so much more to you than that."

At first, I didn't want to listen. I'd spent years training as an engineer, developing project management skills, building teams, weaving together the myriad aspects of organizing, managing, and overseeing multi-million-dollar enterprises. That's what I was good at. Hadn't I proven that?

"Undoubtedly." The voice whispered back. "And now it's time to use all those skills you've gathered in a more meaningful way."

Huh? I thought, by now completely confused, and more than just a little concerned. *What on earth does that mean?*

"You've always wanted to do something that would make a difference in the world, something that will *really* help people," the voice persisted.

Yeah, right! And how am I supposed to do that? I argued back.

"You should open up your own light box center."

What?! I was dumbstruck. *Where on earth is this coming from? Just when I feel like the BIGGEST LOSER, stripped naked, and with nothing to be proud of at this moment, some-*thing *or some-*one *is telling me to open* *my own wellness center? Is it stress? Am I having a psychotic breakdown or something? Because one of us has got to be crazy!*

I have heard that, sometimes, when everything in one's life has turned completely upside down, and nothing seems to make sense anymore and there's nowhere left to turn, it's not uncommon to mistake a breakthrough for a breakdown.

I continued wrestling with the thought, and the voice, adamant that this was too crazy to contemplate. But the voice only grew more persistent.

The next time I bumped into Fred, I found myself announcing, "I think I want to open a light box center." Since I needed training, and he was going through a divorce and didn't have anywhere to live, I suggested he take up temporary residence on the ground floor of my house while he was teaching me what I needed to know. After all, he was the designer of the technology that I wanted to build a business around, and I had a lot to learn.

It soon became apparent that sharing my house with Fred was not necessarily the best dynamic. He'd barely moved in before he started pressuring me daily with questions like, "When am I gonna get my money for the light boxes? When are you gonna pay me? I need money now! Can you lend me money until you can pay me for the light boxes?" Since Fred never seemed to have any money, I paid for everything. I did his laundry, cooked his meals, and I even chauffeured him around because he didn't have a vehicle. It seemed odd to me because Fred was very well dressed. He had expensive tastes in shoes and clothing. It dawned on me that Fred could be a bit of a Jekyll and Hyde character. He was intelligent, inventive, extremely knowledgeable, and capable of immense compassion. At the same time, he also was arrogant, egotistical, imperious, argumentative, and extremely secretive. All of which made Fred a challenging person to live with.

I had calculated it would take several years to save the $300,000 that Fred wanted for two light boxes, plus whatever I would need to open and furnish the Center. He had only been staying with me for a few weeks, but already his constant pressuring for money was weighing on me. I planned to continue working full time until I had saved as much as I could, and then raise the rest to get the Center going. What I hadn't figured on was losing my job when Zeus ran away. I had some money, and a little gold put aside, but with nothing coming in and a dream to fund, things were bound to get worse before they got better.

After a year of not working, I had blown through what was left of my savings. I lost my home and had to file for bankruptcy. Things were not looking very positive, as my country song kept playing. Fred was still living with me and still expecting me to take care of him. So, I used what little money I had left to move us both into a two-bedroom apartment and then borrowed some money from my parents. I was out of options. Either I gave up on the idea of opening the Center, or… it was then that I realized there was no "or" for me. Somewhere along the line, the notion that I could make a difference in the world had gone through a radical transformation. My little "pie-in-the-sky" seed of an idea to open a center had become a full-blown, every-cell-in-my-body-knows-it conviction that *this* was what I was *meant* to do. I didn't know the exact moment it had happened, but opening a wellness center had gone way beyond a dream for me and become a mission. What's more, in stripping away everything I had accomplished, I had utterly lost my ego along with my identity.

There was nowhere else to go and nothing else to do other than surrender to the situation. "Okay, fine, If I'm meant to do this, I'll keep on pursuing it for as long as I am able," I spontaneously declared, as I threw my hands up in the air in an all-or-nothing gesture. Again, I asked for assistance, "If you want me to do this, God, you're going to have to find a way to make it happen. I have no income and no house. I've got this guy living with me who's bugging me every day for money. And you know I don't handle stress too well. And *this* is super stressful."

I needed to figure things out fast. Having already raised millions for the movie project, I knew I could write a compelling business plan for the Center. After conducting the necessary market research, I crafted a layman's explanation of the complicated technology. And then, I outlined my vision for the Center, its aims and objectives, and the conditions I believed we could help. Six people believed in me enough to say, "I'll invest in you." Six more said they would loan me money, but at a high percentage of interest. If I needed proof that my life was finally on the right path, the level of faith that those twelve people were prepared to place in me was evidence enough.

We've all read or heard about such moments… when someone's humble prayers are answered at the eleventh hour in a moment of complete despair and utter surrender. And if you're anything like me, I'll bet that you too have thought, "Yeah, right, I bet it didn't happen quite like that."

But in my case, it really did happen like that. It was as if an invisible energy field that had been blocked had suddenly been freed to start flowing again. I felt more hopeful than I had in a long time. I started reviewing my assets. *What could I do? What was I good at? How could I leverage my skills and experience to get this project moving?*

Within six months, I was open for business! I would never have dreamed things could come together so quickly, but when you are on your path, it seems that neither time nor money is a factor. Nothing was getting in my way.

I kept filtering money to Fred to keep him off my back. I got him to give the go-ahead to his manufacturer to start building my light boxes. I then turned my attention to finding the perfect location in which to house them. With the remaining money, I paid a hefty deposit on the lease of a building I found and bought second-hand furnishings at estate sales, garage sales, and auction houses. With the addition of a few pieces left over from downsizing to the apartment, I managed to outfit the Center.

The Life Center in Westminster, Colorado, first opened its doors on October 20th, 2010—eight days before my 40th birthday. My heart pounded with a blissful mixture of gratitude, satisfaction, and immense relief. The dream of creating something worthwhile that had been tickling my consciousness for many years had finally become a reality. I'd pulled it off. I'd followed my intuition, albeit with some resistance and questioning. I'd stuck it out, and against enormous odds, I had fulfilled what had initially seemed an "impossible dream," to reference one of Elvis's most famous songs.

All I have to do now, I told myself, *is follow the protocol that Fred's laid down, and one day I will be able to say, "Forget automotive. Forget telecommunications. Forget movies. I made a difference in the world by helping sick and hurting people bring their bodies back into a state of balance, and assisting healthy people to remain healthy." And what could be more important than that?!*

It was an exciting and immensely magical moment, and I couldn't help congratulating myself on having reached the pinnacle.

CHAPTER FIVE

Taking Back My Power!

Here we go, I thought. My insides were quivering like jelly with a combination of excitement and trepidation as I welcomed our first client into the newly opened Life Center.

Grateful for the groundwork laid by the buildup of anticipation around the elderly couple's original intention to bring the light box to Colorado, I spread word of its arrival around town and on Facebook. And the calls came flooding in. Jim's phone call had been among them. He had renal failure. We had planned on opening the Center on November 1st. But Jim was desperate, he was worried he was going to die, so we agreed to open up ten days early just for him. I was a little daunted that our very first client should present with such a severe condition, but I knew that Fred would show me what to do.

Even so, I found it hard to contain my shock when Jim showed up for his appointment. One glance at his ashen face and my heart momentarily plummeted. I had never seen skin so grey. But Fred quickly and expertly schooled me on what to do and how to do it, and I was off and running. Excitement bubbled like over-heated blood in my veins, and a sudden flight of "What ifs" buzzed around my brain.

What if we can really help Jim! What if we can really make a difference to his quality of life?! Wouldn't that be cool? Three days later, when Jim returned for his next session, his skin was pink again.

Jim followed Fred's protocol to the letter. Funded by his friends and family, he booked a small series of sessions close together, with a break in between to allow his body to integrate the energy and process the changes. Over the next four months, I witnessed his transformation from a profoundly desperate, frightened man to someone who had found a reason to start enjoying his life again. Then, after he was doing better, he stopped coming, and we lost touch. That's not uncommon. As much as I get attached to some of my clients, and miss them when they stop coming, I've never wanted them to feel they *have* to keep returning *ad infinitum*. I don't want them to be dependent upon the Center for life or me either. I only want them to come until the innate intelligence of their body takes over, and they start healing on their own. We are a resource to help them get their mind, body, or emotions back into a state of wellness, and to help them maintain wellness if they feel they need help with that in the future.

I cannot say whether we could claim to have helped Jim in any medically meaningful way; all I know is what I witnessed over those months. An older, single, man whose skin had turned from grey to pink, and who seemed to me to have regained a bit of spring in his step.

Interestingly, Jim was our only client that first week. But I wasn't worried. I was aware of a deep-seated knowing in my heart and my cells that the Center would be a success because what we were doing was worthwhile.

A week later, a woman came into the Center seeking something, *anything*, that would help her three-year-old son who was fighting his third bout of brain cancer. The moment I looked at the child, it was as if my entire body deflated. I had never encountered such a terrible situation before and felt totally unequipped to cope with it. *He's only three. And already he's fighting his third battle with cancer. I didn't sign up for this! I can't watch this precious child die!*

When I confided to Fred my concerns about attempting to help this child, he looked at me levelly and said, "If you don't help them, who will? Because there are no other opportunities or modalities. This kid's three years old, and this is the third time he's had to deal with brain cancer."

"Okay," I said, meekly, knowing in my heart that we had no choice. It felt significant that this woman, this mother had come to us for help on my 40th birthday. It didn't feel like a coincidence; it felt like synchronicity. The little boy's name was Evan, and each time he visited us over the next seven weeks or so, Fred was unfailingly kind and gentle with him. Sometimes, Evan's grandmother came with him. She told us that Evan couldn't play or eat much, and was always complaining of a pain in his neck. They gave him Tylenol. I had a medical doctor look at his brain scan, and he said, "Gail, this is all tumor. There is no brain."

I was perplexed. "But he's walking, and he's talking. How can he not have any brain?" "I don't know," he replied. "I can only tell you what this scan is showing me. And there's really not a whole lot of brain."

I pondered that for quite a few moments before I came up with an answer that made sense to me. *Okay, then,* I reasoned. *If this little guy can walk and talk and make jokes in different voices, it must mean that we are more than our physical brain, as many of the books I've been studying claim.*

After a few sessions, Evan's grandma came in and said, "I just want to thank you because my grandson has a quality of life he didn't have before. We don't know how long we will have him for, but right now, he's playing in the park, and he's eating chicken McNuggets." Tears slid down my face. I was so grateful that we hadn't turned him away. We couldn't cure Evan. But at least we had made a small difference and given him a little extra quality of life for a while.

Evan passed away just before Christmas. When I heard the news, I broke down and cried for days, saying, "I don't want to do this. I can't see children die. I just can't."

I started to worry that all of our clients were going to prove as tricky as Evan and Jim. I wasn't equipped to take care of these kinds of situations. "What did I get myself into?" I wailed to Fred. "Not all the clients will be such a challenge," he replied calmly. "And, remember, you are not going to save everyone."

Fred taught me how to use the light box. "You just put them in on this or that music setting. Turn the light down or turn it up, and then set your timer for the duration. When you get them out, make sure you ask how they are feeling, tell them to drink plenty of water and have them schedule their follow-up session." He made it sound so easy. Which, of course, it was. I just followed his instructions, and we started getting more and more clients, and by the end of the year, we were in a favorable net income situation.

Fred was a very clever man. He knew a lot about sound and light technologies and how these interact with the body. He also was an extremely gifted clairvoyant who could see what was going on *inside* a person's body.

At first, I didn't believe that he could see into the physical body as clearly as he seemed to do. Convinced that he must be lying about his abilities, I would randomly point to people in the street and ask him to tell me what he could see.

"What do you see with that lady over there?" I'd say, randomly pointing to people in the street, or clients who came into the Center. "The blood flow in her neck is flowing the wrong way," he'd calmly reply. "Well, what about that guy?" I'd press. "There's inflammation in his left kidney," he'd say. "It's swollen." But still, I was skeptical, till one day a girl came into the Center for a session and told us she had cancer.

"No, you don't," Fred said, slowly scanning her body from head to toe "You have fibroids."

"No," she insisted. "I'm a nurse. I don't have fibroids. I have cancer."

"Then I'd get a second opinion," Fred told her with an air of complete confidence.

After she'd followed his advice, the nurse returned to tell us that Fred was right; she had fibroids.

"How do you know?" I asked him later.

Fred shrugged. "I told you: I can see them," he said as if it was no big deal. After that, all I could think was, *I want that gift. I want that gift.* But try as I might—and believe me, I really did try with all my might—I never could *see* in the way that Fred sees. But over time, I did discover that I could *feel*... and I could *hear*.

I recall one particular occasion in 2011 when I was standing among a group of people at an event. They were talking about the brother of a woman in the group who was in the hospital with an infection. Suddenly, clear as a bell, I heard what sounded like the word "staph" in my head. I had learned a great deal about illness and disease since I'd opened the Center. I knew the names, the pathology, the symptoms, statistics, and prognoses of many conditions and ailments, but I didn't, at that point, recognize as a medical condition the word I had heard. All the same, I found myself blurting out, "I think he has a staph infection."

"Oh, my God!" the woman exclaimed. "That's exactly what they're thinking!"

Nowadays, it happens to me all the time. I haven't learned to do it on demand, but I have learned to trust it when it happens. It's not yet 100 percent, and I have to be in the right space, but I'm finding more and more that I'll be having a consultation with a client, and the name or root cause of their issue magically pops into my head. It's been described to me as a mixture of clairsentience and clairaudience. Unlike clairvoyants, who "see" something psychically, either in their imagination or as if they are watching an inner TV screen, clairsentients experience a clear inner "knowing" or "feeling" about objects, people, and situations. Clairaudients, on the other hand, "hear" something psychically, either silently in their head, or auditorily as if someone is actually speaking words in their ear.

One of the most famous clairaudients was the psychic reader and healer, Edgar Cayce, who passed on in 1945. Unusually, however, Cayce could only "hear" the guidance he was getting and share it with others when he was in the sleep state. Hence, he became known as "the Sleeping Prophet."

The Center continued to do well. I continued to do my sessions in the light box as much as was allowed by the protocol. My migraines ceased after about 8 more sessions. They never returned. Some days, I would get so excited that I'd almost want to pinch myself to make sure I wasn't dreaming. It was so much fun to watch people having incredible experiences in the chambers, and the more success stories we witnessed, the happier I felt. *Oh my God, I made this happen, I raised this money. I worked really hard, I opened the Center, and people are coming in and having amazing experiences.* Knowing you've made a positive impact on someone's life is an indescribable feeling. Yes, it's great for the ego. Still, more important is knowing that you have been directly involved in helping others discover a way to ease debilitating conditions or ailments that are preventing them from feeling their best and being able to live a healthy, vibrant life.

Of course, some people came in just to be nosey or to see what their friends were talking about. After all, the light box was unlike anything else they had likely encountered. Those were the types that would often say they didn't have anything that needed fixing; they just wanted to have an "experience." But when I'd question why they hadn't mentioned a long-term issue they'd checked on their intake form, they'd say, "Well, I just thought it was normal at my age." The look of surprise on their faces when they'd come back and tell me, "It's gone. I don't have it anymore," was so gratifying.

Conversely, I would get frustrated when someone couldn't believe you could just "lie in a box with sound and light," and an ailment of 20, 30, or 40 years or more would start to get better. It was hard to accept that people could discount or minimize their own experience by crediting their recovery to something abstract like the weather, or what they ate for dinner the night before. I was so committed to helping people feel better and had witnessed too many successes to doubt the box's ability to help people improve, I naturally wanted them to acknowledge it also, especially when the proof was in the way they felt.

But, as Fred pointed out, I had to let go of *my* expectations and accept that some people would never be convinced. So long as they were leaving the Center feeling better, that was rewarding enough.

There was wisdom in what Fred said, and I learned a great deal from him, for which I shall always be grateful. At the same time, his arrogance and air of superiority were hard to live with. He wanted me to be subservient. He wanted to know everything that I was doing, and he would tell me that he never trained any Centers with *all* the knowledge because he didn't trust them. He would say he retained knowledge so they could not do it on their own. These statements revealed a lot about him.

Since I knew that Fred's ego would disallow him from believing that anything he'd designed could possibly be improved upon (and certainly not by me), I kept my embryonic thoughts and ideas to myself. Fred's constant presence in my life, my home, and my business were becoming increasingly stifling, and it was dawning on me that I had allowed him to stay for so long because I had thought that I needed him, that if he walked away or I kicked him out of the house, the Center would fail. But the truth was, I had allowed Fred to control me, and to take over my home and my business as if he owned them.

In all the time I knew him, I don't think I ever heard any praise from Fred. On the contrary, it seemed that he delighted in putting me down. I felt like he was always chipping away at my confidence, always telling me I was doing things wrong.

"You're the worst student I've ever had," he would jeer. "You don't listen, you just want to do things your own way." And yet, I was doing everything at the Center from management, admin, and budgeting, to working directly with clients. I followed his protocol to the letter, handling publicity, promotions, and social media, cleaning and taking out the trash. And the business was clearly doing exceptionally well. I'd also worked hard at developing my intuitive ability, and was becoming increasingly attuned to what was at the roots of my clients' issues as well as how best to support their healing journeys. So, it felt all the more unjustified when, one day, Fred started berating me again for no apparent reason. This time, instead of meekly accepting his tirade, I completely lost it. Without stopping to think, I just blurted out, "Are you *ever* going to tell me I am doing something right?"

I don't know what I expected him to say, but when he just looked me straight in the eye and coldly and dismissively uttered the word "Nope," I was stunned.

And there you have it, a familiar little voice whispered in my head. *That's the kind of teacher Fred is; he will take what he can, share as little as possible, keep the most important information to himself, and cut you down at every turn so you will never gain the confidence to feel you can do it without him.*

That was the turning point for me. As I chewed it over later in my mind, I had to face facts. I had paid Fred his asking price for the units and then given him even more money whenever his funds were low, which happened with increasing frequency. And I'd sold units to other Centers, for which I'd never received the commissions he'd promised. He had lived rent-free for two years, during which I had taken care of his laundry, his meals, paid the cable bill for his channel subscriptions, and so much more besides. And all without any thanks or show of appreciation on his part.

The truth was staring me in the face. Enough was enough.

In the beginning, I had thought that Fred and I had an equitable relationship. I supported him, and he helped me in return. I provided a place to live and money to live on, and he would teach me to use his technology and share everything he knew with me. It was supposed to be an equal exchange of energy.

But Fred's need to be important kept him from being an outstanding teacher, as he believed that the less he shared with people, the more valuable he was. What he didn't understand, which I was now learning to appreciate, was that when it comes to energy—and everything, including money and information, is energy—the more you share, the more you receive in return.

Fred eventually (albeit reluctantly) moved out almost two years after moving in with me. Though I had looked forward to that day for some time, when it finally arrived, I knew it was actually perfect timing. Working with Fred had taught me a lot, but working with the light box had prepared me even more. I had grown in many ways. Now I felt ready to step into my full power.

It was time to take back the reins of my life and business and start carving out a new and more energetically-aligned path for both my clients and myself.

CHAPTER SIX

There Are No Accidents

Over the years, I had learned a lot about frequency, vibration, and energy (particularly spiritual energy) from books by prominent teachers such as Wayne Dyer, Edgar Cayce, and Dr. Norman Shealy. But it wasn't until I started working with clients at the Center that I experienced the subtle but all-pervasive nature of the energy phenomena these authors and teachers had written and spoken about.

For those not familiar with the term "spiritual energy," let me digress for a moment and briefly explain it. The difference between physical energy and spiritual energy is best summed up by the title of one of Wayne Dyer's book, *You'll See it When You Believe it.* In other words, spiritual energy refers to a level of energy that we cannot perceive because it is higher than our range of frequency. This level of energy runs through everything—humans, animals, plants, and all living things. Throughout history, the wise women, shamans, medicine men, and other practitioners of different cultures and religions have found different ways of harnessing universal life force energy. The Chinese refer to this unseen energy as Chi or Qi. The Hawaiians call it Mana. The Sanskrit word for it is Prana. In the West, it's been referred to by a variety of names, including orgone, ether, entelechy, animal magnetism, and psychic energy. Some modern scientists and skeptics will deny there is any such thing as "spiritual energy." However, a 30-year bioenergy experiment conducted under controlled laboratory conditions by John G. Kruth and William Jones at the Rhine Bio-Energy Lab demonstrated and measured through bio-emissions and bio-photons that universal life energy exists.[6]

When I first experienced the light box in 2007, my interest in subtle energy phenomena and the use of sound and light frequencies as potential healing therapies expanded. I started reading books about energy medicine, resonant frequencies, color therapy, and the anatomy of the body. I studied how the body works with vibrations, how light frequencies change for everybody as well as for different parts of their body, and how musical instruments can heal. I studied the work of the renowned harpist, singer, songwriter, author, and sound therapist, Ani Williams.[7]

I learned how sound has the capacity to affect us on all levels—physical, emotional, mental and spiritual—from the late teacher, performer, and composer, Kay Gardner, whose glorious book *Sounding the Inner Landscape: Music as Medicine*[8] draws upon research into mathematics, chemistry, physics, and ancient cultures to explore the beneficial effects of music. I learned about the healing effects of different instruments, keys, and musical forms from Ani and Kay, as well as which keys stimulate specific areas of the body that govern the immune system, excite the passions or soothe the soul. I also joined an organization called the International Association for Music and Medicine. (IAMM.)[9]

Dr. Dominique Surel is the founder of Noetic Systems International (NSI),[10] and a Noetic scholar trained in Radiesthesia* and Controlled Remote Viewing (CRV). Dr. Surel played a pivotal role in helping me enhance and fine-tune my intuition. Dr. Surel's doctoral thesis focused on the role of intuition in the decision-making process. When I discovered that she had created a proprietary methodology to develop natural intuitive skills, I signed up for her unique training course, which integrates Intuition, Critical Thinking, and CRV to increase awareness, clarity, and quickness in one's decision-making process especially in crisis situations or in solving complex problems.

As my intuition and inner guidance grew stronger, clearer, and more reliable, I started questioning some of the things I had been told about music and light. Some musicians say that the notes and tones of synthesized music have the same effect on us as the notes and tones of real instruments, but my intuition said that it isn't true. There are definitely differences between the two types of music. So, when I read that piano music balances the nervous system, I invited a physician to set up some heart rate variability (HRV) tests. I wanted to see if the piano music I played when clients were in the light box was really affecting their autonomic nervous systems. The physician's report verified it was having a beneficial effect. Of course, I couldn't say the evidence was incontrovertible, as we had to take other factors into consideration. Not the least of which is that merely being in the chamber is a profoundly relaxing experience in itself.

---

*   Radiesthesia is the science of using the vibrational fields of the human body to access information about other objects of animate or inanimate nature by establishing resonance with their energy fields, using specially calibrated instruments and a scale of qualitative measurement to decode this information. Some practitioners use divining rods and/or pendulums to detect the presence of underground oil, gold, minerals, or water, or the nature of an illness or guilt of a suspected person.

But it has to be more than that, I thought as I pondered this conundrum. So, we did some other small experiments. One involved live blood analysis with a dark field microscope to measure the effects of a drumming session on the white blood cell counts of different clients. I always sought physicians and experts to work with me on these experiments. However, since these weren't double-blind clinical trials, which are the only kind that satisfies the medical and scientific communities, we could not claim to be proving anything.

Nonetheless, I knew that something was happening because clients were reporting they were not getting sick so often. The only conclusion I could reach was that the whole-body immersive experience inside the chamber was having a beneficial effect on their bodily systems. And given the hundreds of testimonials I was getting from clients, that made me much happier than pleasing the skeptics ever could.

I continued to educate myself on all the different facets of health and illness. I read a lot of books on emotional trauma. Among the standouts for me was Alison Steadman's *Who's the Matter With Me?* which, considering it was published in the early 1960s, was way ahead of its time,[11] and Karol K. Truman's *Feelings Buried Alive Never Die.*[12] (You can still find copies of both these books on Amazon.) In an attempt to put all the pieces together, I studied iridology and other modalities that looked at the tongue, skin, hair, and/or nails to diagnose deficiencies in energy or nutrition. I studied with several physicians and learned how the liver functions and how to read blood work. Then I delved into Eastern medicine, which taught me about the connection between eczema, psoriasis, acne, and liver issues, as well as gut and brain health.

The more I learned, the sharper my observational abilities became. Between my accumulated knowledge and my now well-honed intuitive skills, I became adept at using all my senses to scan people's energy fields, their body language, demeanor, posture, skin tone, eyes, and facial expressions. Together, the external and subtle signs created a picture of what was ailing them, and I would intuitively know what would best support their well-being.

I was especially fascinated with the sound and light components of the light box experience. I became a research nerd, reading everything I could find on light frequencies and the harmonics of sound and color. The more I understood these, the more excited I got, thinking about how we could adapt the way we utilized these frequencies to enhance the experience.

And then something wholly unexpected happened to propel everything I was doing in a new direction.

Some might call it divine intervention. Others would argue against that, claiming it was just a fluke, a coincidence, or a "lucky" outcome to an "unfortunate" experience. Personally, I believe that there are no such things as "accidents." As for coincidence, well, I prefer the Swiss psychologist, Carl Jung's theory of synchronicity, or meaningful coincidence, which he attributes to "a governing dynamic that underlies the whole of human experience which allows for temporally coincident occurrences of acausal events." But that's just my opinion. I'll tell you the story and let you judge for yourself.

It happened on a cold November day in 2016. It had snowed the night before, but I wasn't overly concerned about driving, as I had learned to drive in Michigan where snow is present many months of the year. I had been to the barn to spend some time playing with my beloved horse, Holly. I had bought her a large activity ball, which she enjoyed pushing around the arena, and I'd been trying to teach her to push a barrel. I left the barn to head back to the Center. I had a couple of clients coming in at 10:30 am, and I wanted to be back in time to open up and turn on some heat for their sessions.

As cold as the temperature was, I felt a warm flush of pride as I sat in the car, reflecting on the great job Holly had done, pushing the barrel for the first time. I started the engine and let it idle for a few moments as I impulsively texted a friend to share my delight at Holly's cleverness. She texted me back instantly, with a friendly warning to not text and drive. "I'm not," I reassured her. "I'm still at the barn, and will be leaving in a few moments."

Having done this drive between the Center and Holly's home at the barn every day since she had come into my life, I was very familiar with the route. Nonetheless, I was mindful of the need for caution. The road was still covered in a layer of snow, and there was a hazy glow that seemed to create an aura around the traffic lights, making them a little harder to see. I didn't know that because the LED bulbs in newer traffic lights don't get hot, snow doesn't melt on them. Instead, it sticks directly to the traffic light casing, which causes a diffusing effect that makes it harder to see whether the traffic light is red, yellow, or green. I was stopped for a light, heading east. I was unaware that the traffic running north to south could not see the color of the lights changing. My light turned green, and so did the green arrow for a large truck alongside me, which was turning left. I proceeded forward.

Looking to my left as the truck cleared from view, I saw a car heading towards me. Unbeknown to me at the time, it was driven by a teenage girl who had only just got her driving license the month before.

Unfortunately, instead of stopping at the red light, the young girl kept on driving. Out of the corner of my eye, I saw her coming. Instinctively, I hit the gas to try and get ahead of her, but I could not outpace her as she was doing somewhere between 45-60 mph.

"What the f—!" I screeched in shock as I heard the sickening sound of metal crunching into metal. My body jerked sideways towards the passenger seat. Then it immediately bounced back as my seat belt responded to the impact of the collision by clamping itself to my chest with steel-like rigidity. Then the car started spinning around and around the intersection.

It happened so quickly, I had no time to register the details. It was as if everything was punctuating my consciousness in ragged staccato-like movements. *A glimpse of my lunch on the floor... Something flying past my head to the back seat (my jacket that was on the passenger seat, I later discovered)... My hands, stiff with numbness from gripping the steering wheel so tightly. The strange litany of sounds—glass breaking, metal folding, horns beeping, the disorienting sensation of spinning, and the heavy pressure on my chest.* Then all of a sudden (or so it seemed to me), someone was yanking the car door open as it suddenly dawned on me: *Shit! I just got hit!*

Still dazed, I looked up at him and blurted out, as if I knew him, "Oh, thank God you're here. I'm so glad you're here." I had no idea who the man was, and yet I was utterly convinced that I did know him.

"What are you saying? You don't know me," he said.

"Yes, I do," I insisted.

He continued looking at me blankly as if I must be suffering from concussion. I couldn't move my neck. My chest was hurting, and I couldn't comprehend that fifteen minutes had passed since the collision. I would have sworn it had been just seconds. "It happened fifteen minutes ago. It wasn't your fault; she ran a red light. It was so brutal to watch what happened to you," he said. Since he had to get to work and could not wait around any longer, he gave me his number in case I needed a witness and left.

When the police arrived, they immediately said I needed an ambulance, I refused. "Oh," one officer said, eyebrows raised in surprise. "Then, you're okay?"

"I am so NOT okay, but I need to get to my office," I said. I didn't bother telling the officer what I did for a living. I was too busy scrolling through my phone, trying to readjust my eyes as everything was blurry. I needed to let my clients know that I had been involved in an accident and would be a little late for our appointment.

It took a while to clear everything up. Once the paperwork was completed, and the police were finally done with me, I headed straight to my office, which was just a short walk from where the accident had occurred. Concerned about my mental well-being, and no doubt worried that I might not make it on my own, one of the policemen kindly accompanied me. My chest hurt, and I still couldn't move my neck, and I was thinking about something I'd read in an article. It had claimed that there's about a six-hour time frame before memories get programmed into the cells. I was desperate to get into the chamber and release the trauma so that my body could start healing itself. When I got to the Center, everyone started fussing around me. My boyfriend, who I'd managed to text after the accident, showed up, wanting to take me home to bed. But we were fully booked with clients, and I couldn't just leave. Then, as luck would have it, one client canceled her appointment. I sighed with relief and gratefully slid right into her spot about four hours after the accident.

One doesn't have to have been in a war zone to suffer PTSD. It can happen to anyone who's experienced any kind of trauma, physical or otherwise. Thanks to the chamber, I recovered remarkably well physically. But still, the reason for the accident, the sheer precision of the timing involved, wouldn't leave me. I couldn't shake off the freakiness of the experience or the knowledge that every single component has to be perfectly orchestrated to within a hairsbreadth of a split-second to result in such a collision. I kept having flashbacks, during which I'd examine each infinitesimal moment in my mind. *I always look both ways. If the truck hadn't been there at that very second... if the snow hadn't stuck to the traffic light and diffused the colors... if I had stayed with Holly for just a few moments longer... if I hadn't stopped to send that text to my friend... If... if... if...*

On top of that, I was struggling to come up with answers to some more critical questions... such as, *Where had I gone in those fifteen lost minutes? What had I been doing? And why had I felt so sure I knew that man?*

I never did get concrete answers to any of those questions. But what happened next convinced me that there must have been a purpose to the accident. For all of a sudden, the design concepts of the Harmonic Egg, and innovations I'd been mentally playing with for some time got strangely more explicit. The vague thoughts and ideas I had been playing with gained more substance, and I found myself coming up with potential solutions that I'd never considered before. Strangest of all, I seemed to have acquired more knowledge about sacred geometry, harmonics, frequencies, and patterns that I was convinced I hadn't read in any book. *How could that be?*

Having read Neale Donald Walsch's *Conversations with God*, and several other books about channeling, I wondered whether that was what was happening with me. *But why? And How?*

Was it possible that the accident had somehow launched me into another reality where all kinds of information were available? Or could it be that my spiritual guides (my reading had taught me that we all have them) were helping me from the other side?

The information seemed to be pouring into and through me. I had no idea where (or whom) it was coming from, there was far too much activity going on in my mind to give any space to contemplate that one. Every day I'd wake up with new aha's and ideas to research or check out on the Internet. And as the pieces of the puzzle started falling into place, I began to sense that I was being given a blueprint for something so revolutionary and evolutionary that it really *might* have the potential to change people's lives. Either I was making it all up, or the dream I'd been nurturing for several years could actually become a real possibility.

Putting on my engineer's hat, I embarked on a frenzy of calculating, drafting, and drawing until my very rough prototype felt perfect. There were certain things that I *knew* were non-negotiable requirements, though I didn't understand *how* I knew them—like, it had to be made of all-natural materials, not metal, nor fiberglass, nor any kind of plastic or synthetic materials, but wood. I also knew, having seen it in a vision, that it had to have the overall look and feel of an egg. At the same time, it had to contain sacred geometry. It resulted in the shape of a dodecahedron (in geometry, a dodecahedron is any polyhedron with twelve flat faces). And it had to be completely smooth and angle free on the inside.

I lost count of the times that I heard people say, "That's impossible!" Or, "It cannot be done. You cannot physically make this device."

I remember telling one naysayer, "Well, Walt Disney said: 'if you can dream it you can do it.' And I've dreamt it."

"Yeah," they were quick to point out. "And you're *not* Walt Disney."

The first manufacturer I approached emphatically agreed with them, telling me that it just couldn't be done.

But I wasn't about to be deterred. I might not be able to see *how* it could be constructed, but I didn't see *why* it couldn't be done. After all, humans are an inventive species. That much is evident from what we've invented and created over the years. So, I just kept on believing and seeking.

And then, as if he'd been conjured up by some invisible hand, or maybe even by the strength of my own belief, a man I'd known for years came into the Center one day and waved a magical wand. His name was Wayman (you read about him in the Introduction). We got to chatting, and without even thinking about it, I just came right out with it… "I got this idea about this wooden egg…" I said as I started to share the story.

To his credit, Wayman didn't even blink once. He listened quietly and with deep interest, and when I got to the part where everyone said it couldn't be done, but I was determined to find a way, he simply said, "Well, then, I'll build it for you."

"You what?! Can you do that?" I exclaimed.

"Well, I don't have any tools," he said. "But if you want to get me some, I'll do it." He seemed so relaxed and matter of fact, which contrasted starkly with the thoughts that were racing through my mind. *What? Just like that? Wayman's going to build it? Why…? How?*

Then he said something that really floored me.

"I feel like it's one of the reasons I was put on this planet—to do this," he said, as casually as if he was explaining why he did any ordinary, everyday task. I was so shocked to hear those words coming out of the mouth of a retired police officer who'd been to West Point and in the military, I was speechless. I spent thousands of dollars on tools. Wayman set to work. And after several months of trying to build my "Egg" without angles inside, he finally conceded defeat. "It just can't be done," he told me sadly.

I couldn't accept it. "No." I cried despairingly. "This has not been given to me to NOT get done. It can work. It has to work. *It has to be done.*"

Wayman left, shaking his head in sorrow and defeat… and then returned a few weeks later, with a triumphant smile on his face, speaking words that were magic to my ears. "I think I know how we can do it."

The timing was perfect, as I had just reached the same conclusion. While Wayman had been gone, I'd been scrolling through Facebook one day when my eyes landed on an image of a strange-looking terrarium situated in a mall or airport building somewhere in England. The plants inside the terrarium had been placed together in a spiral-like shape. There was something about the image that had hooked my attention. As I stared at it with interest, trying to figure out what, specifically, about it had caught my attention, I had the strangest sensation. The only way I can describe it is to say that it felt like wheels had slowly started turning in my head. Then, all of a sudden, it hit me. *Yes! That's it!* I cried out loud, as the solution that everyone said did not exist instantaneously burst into vivid life in front of me. I could see it in my mind's eye as clearly as if I was looking at a high-definition television screen.

I went back to the drawing board and started sending thoughts, ideas, and sketches on the design and structure to Dr. Domique Surel. Using Radiesthesia, she would conduct research on the golden mean ratio, and how you could conserve the golden ratio with parabolic forms. She would also verify for me whether and how specific types of music and sound would work. I loved collaborating with her. She was so methodical and precise, which was just what the engineer in me demanded. Having someone as skillful as Dr. Surel to bounce ideas off, and to give me feedback and guidance was invaluable to me.

I also considered myself very lucky to have found Wayman, who is a genius of a man with the brain and consciousness of a Nikola Tesla. I was impressed by his inventiveness and skill when I learned about some of the wind- and water-powered devices and motors he had conceived and built. Once he and I started working together on the prototype, our energies naturally flowed in perfect sync.

I recall one particular day when Wayman was working on the Egg. He was standing in the center of the construction, where the middle would eventually be. The two ends that he'd already put together bracketed his body on either side. He called to me to turn on the air conditioning, yelling, "It's so hot in here."

"What do you mean," I said, puzzled. "It's not hot in here. It's 90 degrees outside, but I've got the air conditioner on in here." As I looked at him, drenched in sweat, I recalled that when I had first seen the image of the Egg, I'd had a flash of insight that it would be able to eradicate viral loads from the body.

"Oh my gosh!" I shouted back, "It's working already!"

"What do you mean?" Wayman said, baffled.

"The Egg… it's working on you! It's clearing disease from your body!" Based on a few conversations we'd had about Wayman's health, I had already deduced that his body was trying to deal with some kind of bacterial or viral issues, so I knew this had to be so.

I was so excited that over the following weeks I called in several doctors, shamans, and highly sensitive people to "test" the Egg energetically as we were building it. I didn't prime them with any information about what I thought or hoped it could do. I just invited them to experience it and tell me what they experienced or "got."

This surprises some, but healers also need healing. Clients at the Center range from medical doctors, DOs, NDs, psychologists, acupuncturists, massage therapists, channelers, shamans, and more. During the process of birthing the Harmonic Egg, many of those clients gave me their intuitive "hits." Two healers who were instrumental in the development of the Egg, who have since become very good friends, are Andye Murphy and Robin Wiggs. Both Andye and Robin spent many hours consulting with me about energy and the way sessions would be conducted in the Egg.

I must confess that when the prototype was complete, I thought it was the ugliest prototype ever. As skilled as Wayman was in many areas, wood-work was not his forte. The prototype looked like it might fall apart at any second. Still, it was constructed to the correct dimensions for testing. It was smooth on the inside. The door opened (though we did have to prop it up to keep it open), and although the lights were just dangling haphazardly, they worked. Best of all, everyone who sampled it, without exception, said the same thing: they could feel enormous power in the Egg.

Since Wayman couldn't take the project any further, I called Daryl and Tony Markel at the manufacturing company I had initially spoken with. Unable to keep the grin off my face, I said with exaggerated casualness, "Hey, I got an Egg in my office."

There was silence at the other end of the phone, "Did I lose you, Daryl?" I prompted, "Can you hear me now?" Several long seconds passed before I finally heard Daryl say, "You mean you actually built one?"

"Yup. We built one." I told him proudly.

To his credit, Daryl didn't laugh or scoff. He just said, "I need to see this." And then promptly drove from Kansas to my Center in Denver to see for himself this engineering marvel of a machine that "could not be built"—but had been.

When he saw the Egg that Wayman built, Daryl was in awe. "You did this?" he said to Wayman.

"Yep."

"Well, then," he declared, "We can do it."

After thoroughly examining the Egg, Daryl calculated where they might encounter issues with the curves, and problems with the door fitting, and so on. Then he took out his phone, and started videoing the interior of the structure, and then called his son, Tony, and streamed what he was filming. Daryl didn't hold back on his excitement.

"Take a look at this… and this… and look at this," he kept saying. "Yep, we can do that… and that…" I heard Tony concurring.

It was one of the most satisfying and gratifying days of my life.

~

"So, what is it about the Egg that makes it so magical?" I'm sure you're wondering.

Countless people have asked me this question. For obvious reasons, I cannot give away all its secrets—the patent is still pending, and the information is proprietary.

What I will say is that none of the factors I was guided to incorporate into the structure of the Egg—like sacred geometry, platonic solids, the golden mean, numerology, Tesla's 3-6-9 theory, the specific frequencies of numbers, light, shape, and sound—are new to humankind. We only have to look at the construction of the pyramids and other ancient edifices to know that throughout history different races and cultures possessed advanced levels of knowledge and technology. But somehow that information got lost in the mists of time, although many would argue that this knowledge was not lost at all. Instead, it was deliberately supressed, because of misuse and the arrogance of those who chose to harness these technologies for power or personal gain.

Thanks to recent technological advancements in medical science, however, many of these ancient beliefs, tools, and systems are enjoying a renaissance and are now being subjected to rigorous scientific testing.

In Part II, we shall explore what the latest science reveals about frequencies, light, color, sound, vibroacoustic therapy, and vibrational energy medicine. And we shall also look at something that I, and many others, regard as fundamental to the success of any form of healing—intention!

But before we get to that…

Whatever Happened to TQ?

For whatever reason, I had set TQ up in my mind as my "big test case." In retrospect, I laugh at my foolishness. Why I'd held so doggedly to the idea that I needed "one, big, irrefutable piece of proof" of the Egg's ability to transform people's lives, I'll never know. The truth is, I'd already had more than enough evidence of that with other clients. Moreover, I was already learning that as much as I (and many others) regard the Harmonic Egg as something of a "miracle chamber," in reality, few transformations occur instantly. The Harmonic Egg is a powerful device. I believe it works on very subtle levels, and people need time to integrate their experiences in it.

In TQ's case, it took a little while, and the process wasn't without its tussles. Initially, he showed much resistance. He wasn't happy about changing his diet. He didn't want to listen to any advice. It wasn't until I got really tough with him and told him in no uncertain terms that if he wanted to have a chance at surviving, he had to listen to me. And if he couldn't do that, then there was no point in wasting his money or my time by coming back.

Fortunately, TQ listened.

To date, TQ has shed over 165 pounds (and is still losing weight). He has not needed dialysis. His heart increased in size by a centimeter, which is something that neither we nor the VA can figure out. His kidneys are functioning well, and also have grown in size. One that was actually non-functioning is now working. He no longer has to rely on a wheelchair to get around and is enjoying walking again. When I met him, his feet were numb, and now he has feeling in them again. His PTSD has improved, and he now has an entirely different outlook on life. Although he is still taking some prescription medications, he is working towards weaning off them.

TQ shared with me that whenever he goes to the VA, they treat him like a hero. They do not understand how and why he is still alive, and continue to ask him what he is doing that his former comrades did not do. He hasn't told them about the Harmonic Egg; he thinks they won't understand. He merely says that he wants to live, and is putting effort into getting healthy. He continues to come for monthly sessions.

TQ tells me I saved his life. I tell him, "No, you saved your life because you listened, and you took action."

PART II

Ancient Secrets, Modern Research

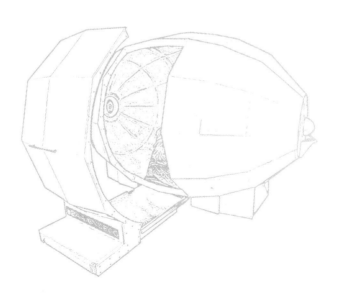

CHAPTER SEVEN

Believe It, and You'll See It

There is a famous quote made by the 19th Century German philosopher, Arthur Schopenhauer, which states that "All truth passes through
three stages. First, it is ridiculed. Second, it is violently opposed. Third, it is
accepted as being self-evident."

I think of this quote whenever I speak to someone who is encountering
the Harmonic Egg for the first time. It never fails to bring a smile to my
face, because just as Schopenhaur says about truth, there are usually three
stages to people's responses to the Egg.

Their first reaction is generally one of confusion, as their brains franti-
cally try to figure out what this enormous, futuristic, egg-shaped chamber
could possibly be. Some are surprised into silence, while others can't stop
exclaiming or even just burst into tears. But whether they voice it out loud,
or just wear the thought on their faces, it's clear they are thinking something
very like "What... the... *Bleep!* ... is... *THAT?!*"

Their second reaction usually consists of a few moments of flip-flopping
between fascination, wariness, intrigue, and total disbelief.

And their third reaction, which often follows after I've given them a very
brief overview, is to ask something like this: "So, how can a chamber that is
furnished with just a zero-gravity chair, a simple sound system, and a variety
of colored lights help people recover from such a diverse range of ailments
as the testimonials on your website suggest?"

The answer to that is the reason I am writing this book.

As with anything that creates a paradigm shift in our thinking,
explaining how the Egg can accomplish physical, emotional, mental, and
spiritual transformation cannot be explained in just a few sentences.

The inimitable philosopher, systems theorist, architect, and inventor,
Buckminster Fuller, once famously said, "You never change things by
fighting the existing reality. To change something, build a new model that
makes the existing model obsolete." That, for me, sums up the Egg.

In this section, I shall be presenting research on several critical components of the Egg. We shall look at the science behind vibrational energy,
the frequencies of sound, light, color, and the power of your thoughts and

emotions, as well as your beliefs and intentions. And we shall see how they combine with other components of the Harmonic Egg to create the necessary environment for transformation to occur.

By the time you have finished reading it, I trust you will understand why I, and many others who have experienced the Egg, believe it's the first in a new generation of non-invasive, therapeutic healing devices that have the potential to make our current "Medical Model" not necessarily obsolete, but certainly less relevant. You will also understand why it offers new options for people to choose from for their health.

> *"Ninety-nine percent of all that is going to affect our tomorrows*
> *is being developed by humans using instruments*
> *and working in ranges of reality that are non-humanly sensible."*
> — BUCKMINSTER FULLER

To understand the power of the Harmonic Egg, let's first look at energy.

What is Energy?

We are fortunate to live at a time where science has the necessary tools and technology to be able to explore and explain so much of what used to be hidden from us. For centuries, the consensus was that we are separate beings, living in a universe occupied by a few other separate objects, like the sun, the moon, the planets, and stars. And in between, there's nothing but empty space.

Recently, however, scientists have begun to discover that far from being completely empty, space is brimming with energy. In fact, energy is one of the real constants of the universe because it is, quite literally, everything and everywhere, and all forms of energy have fields. So, space is filled with quantum fields of energy from particles, waves, quarks, electrons, photons, and doubtless much more that we are yet to understand.

Studies demonstrate that just like fish swimming in the ocean, we are swimming in a sea of energy in which we are continually being bombarded by waves of frequencies or vibrations at all times. Nothing in the universe can happen without energy being involved. It is the building block of *all* matter, regardless of whether we perceive that "matter" as something that is living or not. So, the energy that composes a living entity or organism, such as a tree, a plant, an animal, and you, is the same energy that composes a non-living entity, like a brick, a house, or a rock. We, too, are made up of a multidimensional mix of vibrating energies that are continually changing with our moods, our physical state of health, what we consume, and even how we think and feel. The same is true of every organ and system in our body. Although science doesn't yet know how it is happening, it can now measure that our thoughts and emotions are literally being transmitted beyond our bodies to others through these fields at all times.

Energy cannot be created, and it cannot be destroyed. It can only be transmuted into another form, which it is doing all the time. It also comes in many forms. There is a kind of energy called kinetic energy in objects that are moving. There is something that scientists call potential energy in objects at rest, like a rock that is being held in place by a wedge. As you are reading this, your body is using metabolic energy from the last meal you ate to break down, synthesize, and transport nutrients and molecules to various parts of your body. Energy can also travel in the form of electromagnetic waves, such as heat, light, radio, and gamma rays.

Energy has one sole job, and that is to make things happen. To accomplish this, it needs to be in constant motion. The more cycles energy completes in the space of one second, the higher its frequency. When the vibration slows down, energy becomes physical matter that appears solid. But if you could look inside that solid object, you would see billions of vibrating subatomic particles continually moving and "popping" with energy.

We humans are meant to be fluid like water, not dense like sludge or solid like ice. Energy needs to flow within us, through us, and around us freely, if we want to remain healthy. If we remove energy from water by reducing its temperature, its vibration will slow down until it becomes solid matter—i.e., ice, which is dense in form and heavy in weight. If we raise the temperature of ice, we speed up its vibration. Eventually, it will turn back into liquid water. If we increase its vibration by adding more heat to water, it will boil and ultimately transform into steam, which is weightless, formless, and almost invisible to the naked eye.

Another demonstration of this can be found in rotating objects that have spokes or blades, such as wheels, propellers, and electric fans. When not in motion, the blades of an electric fan are quite solid and visible, but when they are moving, it becomes harder to make out each individual blade. And when they are rotating faster than our brain can perceive, the blades seem to "disappear" altogether, allowing us to see right through to the other side. But just because we can no longer see them, it doesn't mean they are not there.

If we live our lives in a low-frequency environment, thinking low-vibrational thoughts, eating low-energy foods devoid of nutrition, and surrounding ourselves with negative-minded people whose fears, doubts, and lack of joy drain our energy, the more slowly our energy will flow in all the systems our body relies on for optimal health and well-being. And the denser our energy becomes, the more we risk it "freezing" in areas of our body, which, ultimately could create blockages, not just in our physical body, but also in our higher, emotional, psychological and spiritual bodies.

Conversely, when we eat fresh foods and vegetables that were grown in healthy soil and surround ourselves with uplifting, joyful people, the faster we vibrate and the higher our frequency becomes. Just like the individual instruments that make up an orchestral performance, the subtle vibrations of our thoughts, feelings, intentions, emotions, and actions also contribute their own vibrational templates to the overall frequency pattern we emit on a daily basis. Whether we are conscious of it or not, we are continually broadcasting the chorus of frequencies and vibrations that make up our overall blueprint, or frequency signature, to those around us.

Likewise, our senses are always picking up on the frequencies that are being emitted by everything and everyone around us. For example, we absorb physical energy from our food, water, and our physical environ-ment. And we absorb emotional and mental energy from the people we live and work with, the media, and the attitudes reflected by our community and mass consciousness. We also take in and give out life force energy (also known as prana, chi, Qi, Ki or bio-energy) through our breath and our chakras. And we are regularly being fed and nurtured by the spiritual energy we receive from our higher selves or our soul.

Together, these energies not only make up the fabric of our physical bodies, but also our higher mental, emotional, and spiritual bodies, which are part of the multi-layered energy system that is the etheric blueprint of what and who we are. When any of these energies are out of balance, the free flow of energy through our physical, mental, emotional, or spiritual (etheric) bodies is constricted, and we become unhealthy in some way. This is where dis-ease begins.

Energy and Consciousness

Throughout history, shamans and indigenous cultures have believed that all energy has consciousness and that it comes from a single source. Experiments with subatomic physics have shown that light and other energies can react to and become influenced by human consciousness. This was confirmed by the famous double slit experiment,[13, 14] which demonstrated that physical light behaves as a particle when we place our attention directly upon it, and as a wave when it is not being observed. In other words, it is aware of our attention and reacts accordingly.

We, too, are hard-wired to absorb and respond to the subtler spiritual energies or frequencies emitted by those around us. Whether we do it unconsciously via resonance (i.e., frequency matching) or entrainment (when part of our system is induced to match a stronger external vibration), or by deliberately tuning into someone in our environment, the result is the same. A transference of energy takes place, which enables us energetically to receive "information" or "impressions" from others. Whether we acknowledge this or not, we are all doing it all of the time.

If you doubt this applies to you, take a few moments to consider the following questions:

- Have you ever been with someone who is acting and speaking as if everything in their life or work is pleasurable and rewarding? Yet, for some reason, you didn't believe them? Something "told you" that beneath their bright façade, they were actually unhappy or anxious about something?

- Have you ever walked into a room in which you later discovered that people had recently been arguing and actually *felt* a heaviness in the air?

- Have you ever found yourself thinking about a friend you haven't seen or spoken to in a long time? Then out of the blue, they write you or call you to say you just popped into their mind out of nowhere, and they felt compelled to reach out.

- And then there's this common one: How many times have you correctly identified the person calling you before you've answered the phone?

Experiences like these are much more common than most of us realize. Instead of dismissing them as a fluke or coincidence, we need to recognize them as evidence of the existence of subtle energies that connect us to one another.

The point I am making here is that we are powerful beings, and the frequency of every thought, feeling, and emotion we have is like a cosmic wave of energy that travels through time and space and even physicality. And, as many spiritual teachers point out: thoughts are electric, emotions are magnetic. So, the more emotion we attach to a thought (negative or positive), the more potent the vibration we send out into the Universe, and the more the same resonant energy, positive or negative, is attracted to us in return. Like attracts like—this is resonance in action; this is how we communicate with the Universe. And this is why it's essential to cultivate a positive view of life and develop an awareness of our thoughts and feelings. Because what we choose to think and feel, and how we live our lives, have profound impacts on what we will experience and how our lives will be. We need to be mindful. If we are constantly beaming out and receiving information, without being aware of it, what might we achieve if we trained ourselves to become conscious of our thoughts and words, and used them for healing both ourselves and others?

Your Energy, Thoughts, Emotions, and Your Health

In February 1999, a research professor in the Department of Physiology and Biophysics at Georgetown University Medical Center in Washington, D.C., named Candace Pert published a book called *Molecules of Emotion: The Science Behind Mind Body Medicine.*[15] Dr. Pert's pioneering research on how the chemicals inside our bodies form a dynamic information network that links our mind and body was considered revolutionary because it provided proof that our thoughts literally change the chemistry of every cell in our body.

Dr. Pert's subsequent books and audios, which include *Your Body is Your Subconscious Mind, Everything You Need to Know to Feel Go(o)d,* and *Psychosomatic Wellness,* and her appearance in the seminal movie *What the Bleep Do We Know?!* reflect her continuing discoveries that mind, body, and spirit cannot be separated. Our emotions literally can transform our bodies and create our health. Dr. Pert's research further convinced her that not only are we hard-wired for bliss, which is both physical and divine, but also that feeling good and feeling God is one and the same.

By the time she died in 2013, Dr. Pert had become a leading proponent of the unity of mind and body, and the ability of emotions to affect health. She counseled: "Since emotions run every system in the body, don't underestimate their power to treat and heal."

1999 was also the year that Japanese researcher Dr. Masaru Emoto published the first in a series of books about how the influence of our thoughts, words, and feelings on molecules of water can positively impact the earth and our personal health.[16] Using high-speed photography, Dr. Emoto discovered that crystals formed in frozen water reveal changes when specific, concentrated thoughts are directed toward them. He found that water from clear springs and water that has been exposed to loving words showed brilliant, intricate, and colorful snowflake patterns. In contrast, polluted water, or water exposed to negative thoughts, forms incomplete, asymmetrical patterns with dull colors and no real pattern.

Dr. Emoto was also responsible for another well-known experiment known as the "rice experiment," in which he demonstrated the power of both negative thinking and positive thinking. After placing portions of cooked rice into two containers, Dr. Emoto wrote the words "Thank you" on one container, and "you fool" on the other. He then instructed school children to say the labels on the jar out loud every day when they passed them by. After 30 days, the rice in the container with positive thoughts was said to have barely changed, while the rice in the other jar was moldy and rotten.

Dr. Emoto's subsequent book, *The Hidden Messages in Water*, became a New York Times best-seller, despite several prominent skeptics and commentators vehemently criticizing him for "designing his experiments in ways that leave them prone to manipulation or human error influencing the findings."

Fast forward to March, 2005, when renowned cellular biologist, international speaker, and now best-selling author, Bruce Lipton [17] radically changed our understanding of life, and how we all think about our own thinking. His pioneering book *The Biology of Belief: Unleashing the Power of Consciousness, Matter & Miracles* was hailed by Deepak Chopra as "providing a much-needed scientific framework for the mind body spirit connection."

Bruce Lipton's insights and research created the basis of the epigenetic revolution that is now laying the foundation for a consciousness-based understanding of our biology. *The Biology of Belief* shared stunning new discoveries that revealed how the cells of our bodies are affected by our thoughts. It demonstrated how the new science of epigenetics is revolutionizing our understanding of the link between mind and matter, and the profound effects this has on our personal lives as well as the collective life of our species. The central message of this book (which in my estimation should be required reading for every human being as soon as they are old enough to understand it), is that, contrary to what science had postulated, we are not our DNA. Our genes do not control our biology. Instead, our DNA is controlled by signals from outside the cell, including the energetic messages emanating from our beliefs and our positive and negative thoughts. What's more, our bodies can be changed as we retrain our thinking.

Given Bruce Lipton's research (along with all the subsequent studies that confirm his findings), and the fact that humans are comprised of at least 70 percent water, I am certainly inclined to give credence to Dr. Masaru Emoto's assertions. Positive thoughts and intentions can not only enhance our own health and well-being, but also create more peace in the world.

Dr. Larry Dossey is a distinguished physician who, like Bruce Lipton, has become an internationally influential advocate of the mind in health and the role of spirituality in healthcare. The former executive editor of the peer-reviewed journal *Alternative Therapies in Health and Medicine*, Dr. Dossey speaks at international conferences on spirituality, health, consciousness, and the future of medicine.[18]

In a conversation about his book *The Extraordinary Power of Ordinary Things* with podcast host, Duncan A. Campbell, Dr. Dossey said that while inherited diseases are an undeniable fact of life, "fully 75 percent or so of our health is going to be determined not by genetics, but by the decisions and choices we make, and the behaviors that we choose to engage in." What's more, he stressed, "it's really important to keep our eye on the ball here. If we don't, we're going to get in a situation where we think that our choices and our consciousness really don't make all that much difference. Nothing, from a health point of view, could be more disastrous."[19]

As the work of Candace Pert, Bruce Lipton, Larry Dossey, and many others confirms, our lives are not run by luck or coincidence. They are run by how we think, feel, and act, and how we communicate with the universe through our vibrations.

Mind Over Matter – The Power of the Placebo Effect

We've all heard of the Placebo Effect, the phenomenon in which some people experience a benefit from a sham treatment or an inactive substance, which they believe to be a genuine treatment for a health condition.

Researchers use placebos during studies to help them understand what effect a new drug or treatment might have on a particular condition. Participants are divided into two groups; one receives the medication or treatment that's being tested, while the other group gets a placebo. Neither group knows whether they got the real treatment or the placebo. Researchers then compare the effects of the drug and the placebo on the people in the study to determine the effectiveness of the new drug and check for side effects.

I've always been fascinated by this subject, which seems such a paradoxical phenomenon, for several reasons. First, because people can respond positively or negatively to a placebo, which means that their symptoms may improve, or they may experience adverse side effects. Second, because there are some conditions in which a placebo can produce results even when people are totally aware that it's a placebo.

Studies show that placebos can have an effect on conditions such as depression, pain, sleep disorders, menopause, and irritable bowel syndrome. An article about placebos on WebMD reports that in one study involving asthma, participants using a placebo inhaler did no better on breathing tests than sitting and doing nothing. But when researchers asked for people's perceptions of how they *felt*, the placebo inhaler was reported as being as effective as medicine in providing relief.[20]

With the emergence of new evidence that our minds can influence the energies of physical matter, including our own physiology, the Placebo Effect is finally getting the attention it deserves. Ted Kaptchuk is a professor of medicine and professor of global health and social medicine at Harvard Medical School and author of the book *The Web That Has No Weaver: Understanding Chinese Medicine*. He's also the Director of the Harvard affiliated Program in Placebo Studies and the Therapeutic Encounter at Beth Israel Deaconess, which is the first multidisciplinary institute dedicated to studying how the Placebo Effect works.[21]

As the article on the Placebo Effect on WebMD states, one of the most common theories suggests that it's down to the person's expectations. If a person expects a pill or procedure to do something, it's possible that the body's own chemistry can cause effects similar to what a medication might have caused. But, says WebMD, "that doesn't mean that it is imaginary or fake, because studies have shown that the Placebo Effect can cause actual physical changes in some cases."

Judith Simon-Prager, PhD and Judith Acosta, LISW are co-authors of *Verbal First Aid: Help Your Kids Heal from Fear and Pain and Come Out Strong.* Their book quotes Dr. Larry Dossey as saying, "Images create bodily changes—just as if the experience were really happening. For example, if you imagine yourself lying on a beach in the sun, you become relaxed, your peripheral blood vessels dilate, and your hands become warm, as in the real thing." [22]

In an article titled "*The Placebo Prescription*," published in *New York Times Magazine*, writer Margaret Talbot confirms that "the placebo effect is not limited to the subjective sensations of patients; some studies show actual physiological change as a result of sham treatments." She cites one study where doctors painted patients' warts with brightly colored, inert dye and promised them their warts would be gone when the color wore off. Sure enough, the patients' warts disappeared just as predicted. [23]

So, What is the Mechanism Behind The Placebo Effect?

Dean Radin, Ph.D., is chief scientist at the Institute of Noetic Sciences, and author of the books, *The Conscious Universe, Entangled Minds: Extrasensory Experiences in a Quantum Reality,* and *Real Magic: Ancient Wisdom, Modern Science, and a Guide to the Secret Power of the Universe.* In his tribute to Dr. Larry Dossey's book, *Reinventing Medicine: Beyond Mind-Body to a New Era of Healing,* which provides the scientific and medical proof that the spiritual dimension works in therapeutic treatment, Dr. Radin says: "The practice of medicine is in the midst of the most astonishing revolution since the germ theory of disease. This revolution doesn't depend on lavish new technologies or tinkering with genes, and it goes far beyond acknowledgment of mind-body connections." [24]

A study at the University of Michigan, published in the August 24, 2005 edition of the Journal of Neuroscience claims that just *thinking* that a medicine will relieve pain is enough to prompt our brain to release its own natural painkillers, and soothe painful sensations. [25, 26]

So, if our brains can produce a similar substance to the one we believe we are taking, the Placebo Effect is not only "in our minds," it's in our bodies too. This means that, whenever we require healing, all we need do is believe that our body knows how to heal itself. Since what we *think* and *believe* can affect how we *feel*, it will also influence how we *heal*.

I am neither a scientist nor a physician. Still, I wouldn't be at all surprised if, one day, "wishful thinking," "mind over matter," and "belief" are recognized as the most potent healing aids of all. Perhaps, as Candace Pert alludes in the title of her powerful meditative audible book/CD, one day, we will all be harnessing the power of our minds, and of the Placebo Effect, by practicing Psychosomatic Wellness.

CHAPTER EIGHT

Sound and Light – Why the Future of Medicine Lies in the Past

For centuries, mystics have been saying that sound creates matter and that the world is a reflection of infinite combinations of sound patterns. They say that all things from the biggest planet to the smallest seed are coagulations of sound waves. Some scientists argue that the galaxies are not arranged at random but in a regular pattern of clusters. Now researchers are suggesting that it was primordial sound waves that helped create this pattern of clusters.[27]

Jewish, Hindu, and Buddhist mystics believe that the Word creates and pervades everything that exists. In the Bible, John wrote, "In the beginning was the Word, and the Word was with God, and the Word was God." Interestingly, the same idea is expressed in the ancient Hindu Vedas, except there, the word "God" is replaced by the word "Brahman."

The spoken word, in the form of prayers, mantras, and chants is at the heart of the world's spiritual traditions. Perhaps the practice is so widespread because people of many religions instinctively recognize the effectiveness of spoken prayer.

But what if it's not the words of the prayer, the chant, or the mantra that matters? But the frequency of the belief and the intention behind the words, coupled with the vibration of the sound?

Could both the Bible and the Vedas have been describing, long before science, how the universe works?

Whether it's the gentle sound of waves lapping on the shore, the hammering of rain on a windowpane, the high-pitched humming of a crystal bowl, or the deep reverberation of a didgeridoo, sounds affect us in different ways. For centuries, various cultures have harnessed the power of sound and vibrations to transform states of mind and being, and to soothe the emotions, balance the mind and body, and facilitate healing. Sound therapy is one of the oldest forms of healing known to man.

The Australian aboriginal people are the first known culture to heal with sound. Some say they've been using the didgeridoo as a tool to treat broken bones and diseases for over 40,000 years. Egyptian and Babylonian cultures used the low-frequency sounds of drums and rattles to speed up healing. According to a Greek traveler named Demetrius from circa 200 B.C., the Egyptians also used vowel sounds and instruments in their rituals.

According to the Greek philosopher, Pythagoras, who lived around 2,500 years ago, music contributes significantly to health… if used in the right way. Pythagoras was regarded as the Father of Harmonics. He studied the distance between notes (musical intervals or the silence between the frequencies is very important to the way music is used to heal). And he realized that sound and harmonics could heal. His healing method, which he called "Musical Medicine," used different intervals of harmonic ratios to treat the physical body and the soul and emotions of patients with music.

Pythagoras developed a special connection with the Cosmos and worked with the vibrational fields of the heavenly bodies, using different musical intervals and harmonic ratios to perform "soul adjustments" by aligning souls with their divine nature. Certain melodies were composed to cure the passions of the psyche, such as anger and aggression. Greek gods that used music therapy were Asclepius and his father Apollo. Asclepius was known as the God of Medicine, and Apollo was regarded as the god of sun, music, light, and prophecy. In Greek mythology, Asclepius was raised by the Centaur Chiron, who taught him medicine and the healing arts. In Egyptian culture, they believe that Asclepius was able to cure illnesses of the mind through music and song.[28]

I was recently in Greece exploring the history of these gods and trying to learn more about the healing of other cultures. Instruments featured in many of the depictions, and in the museums, I saw old flutes that were used. It was quite fascinating to go to the sites that were mentioned to be hospitals, built thousands of years ago and hundreds of years BC. It blew my mind.

Technological sound healing devices first appeared in 1928 when German scientist Erwin Schliephake discovered that sound waves accelerated healing. When sound waves are applied to the body, the cells and tissues absorb some of the energy, thereby increasing circulation.[29]

Dr. Royal Raymond Rife is credited with being one of the most forward thinkers in the 20th century for his use of vibrational energy, or sound frequencies, to cure cancer. He wrote about this extensively in his book, *The Cancer Cure That Worked.* But as with many others who have found non-invasive, drug-free treatments for diseases like cancer, Rife was shut down by the American Medical Association.[30]

How Sound Healing Might Work on the Body and the Brain

It's believed that resonance may be the most important principle of sound healing. In the context of healing humans or animals, it can be described as the frequency of vibration that is most natural to a specific organ or system such as the heart, liver, or lungs. Everything has a frequency at which it naturally resonates. This is known as the Prime Resonance Frequency (PRF). Our bones, cells, and organs all have their own PRF. For example, the PRF of a typical cell is 1000 hertz, while the PRF of a heart is around 100 hertz. The resonance principle relates to the cellular absorption of the healing sounds and/or their harmonics. In sound healing, resonance principles are employed to re-harmonize cells that have become unbalanced as a result of toxic substances, emotional traumas, or pathogens, etc. In my view, there is no set frequency for each and every person, these are only general industry "guesses." I believe the higher the person vibrates, the more "off" these general industry guesses will be for them.**

Dr. James Gimzweski, of UCLA, California, has revolutionized the study of cellular function by using an atomic force microphone to listen to the sounds emitted by cells. In focusing on mapping the pulsations of the cell's outer membrane, Dr. Gimzweski's new science, which is called sonocytology, has revealed that every cell in our bodies has a unique sonic signature and "sings" to its neighbors. Sonocytology is being hailed as a powerful diagnostic tool for identifying the sounds of healthy cells versus those of unhealthy ones. Cells are fed and communicate through cellular ion channels. If the cells are not healthy, their channels may close or become obstructed. The theory is that music/sound vibrations can open up the channels, which enables the cells to be fed and to communicate again. Dr. Gimzweski has demonstrated that sound can open channels in the cells and restore health. This is achieved by greatly amplifying the destructive sounds of unhealthy cells and playing them back to the cells so that they implode and are destroyed. Since healthy cells would not resonate with these frequencies, the surrounding tissue remains undamaged.[31]

** Rife's method was to analyze the cells of individual patients and determine what frequencies would work for their body. Today, however, most Rife practitioners rely on a system of preset numbers and frequencies, which I am not convinced is as effective. Also, some practitioners still believe that the frequencies which Rife determined killed cancer 80 years ago will also kill cancer today. Personally, I am not convinced this still holds true. I believe that cancer has mutated over the past 80 years, and is different for each individual.

Music and Health Research

Dr. Dominique Surel, who wrote the foreword to this book and whose knowledge and expertise proved so helpful in my development of the Harmonic Egg, is the Dean of Faculty and a professor at Energy Medicine University (EMU, California). A Council Member of the Society for Scientific Exploration (SSE) and Co-Founder of the World Institute for Scientific Exploration (WISE), Dr. Surel not only teaches Master and PhD level courses at EMU in Critical Thinking, Leadership, Intuitive Intelligence™, Controlled Remote Viewing, and Radiesthesia, but also conducts trainings and lectures internationally on Human Potential.[32]

In 2015, Dr. Surel gave a lecture on the Power of Sound and Music at a conference in Helsinki, in which she shared evidence from a slew of scientific studies which show that:

- Listening to music releases endorphins, which increase the body's tolerance to pain and reduce stress.

- A study published in the *Journal of Pediatrics* in April 2013 looked at what happens when mothers sing lullabies to premature babies. Monitors showed that music reduced the stress levels of the babies; their heartbeats slowed, they became calmer, and oxygen saturation increased.

- 30 minutes of classical music produces the same effect as 10 mg of Valium (Baltimore Hospital Coronary Care Unit study).

- Rock music causes people to eat more food and to eat it faster (Johns Hopkins University).

In her Helsinki lecture, Dr. Surel spoke about the work of French musician, composer, acupuncturist, and researcher, Fabien Maman, who was the first person to link music with acupuncture. He created the system which uses tuning forks instead of needles on acupuncture command points. Maman described Sound Therapy as a "treatment based on the finding that human blood cells respond to sound frequencies by changing color and shape." Maman hypothesized that sick or rogue cells can be healed or harmonized by sound.[33]

Fabien Maman observed that human cells each have a specific vibrational frequency that corresponds to a sound. Likewise, each individual has a unique sound or vibrational signature with which he/she resonates. This sound carries the energy and resonance of consciousness and life, which makes it more potent than any other type of sound. Maman believes this could explain why one specific healing sound might not have the same effect on every person. He was able to affect the shape of a cell by using acoustic sounds. Acoustic instruments are more effective than electrical instruments/synthetic sounds in terms of healing humans because they produce more harmonics. Acoustic guitars have a soundbox that generates resonance. In contrast, the electric guitar has a flat box and only half the resonance. Maman maintained that it is the harmonics that reach and affect human cells, not the sounds themselves.

Pure sound can destroy cells such as cancer. Cancer cells show evidence that their cell nuclei are incapable of maintaining their structure when sound wave frequencies attack the cytoplasmic and nuclear membranes.

In Maman's research, nine musical notes were played on a xylophone for fourteen minutes. Resonance started in the middle of the cell and progressed outward. At the end of fourteen minutes, the cancer cells became disorganized and broke up.

When the experiment was repeated with a human voice, the cancer cells disorganized, disintegrated, and then exploded after nine minutes.

Music and Memory

According to Dr. Surel, research conducted by Dr. Stork and Dr. Mosqueda, Director of Geriatrics at the University of CA, Irvine into Alzheimer's disease and dementia showed that when patients listen to a piece of music they had heard when they were young, their eyes suddenly become alive. Some even start to tap their feet to the beat of the music and start talking about that time in their lives. They can remember events and emotions. Some even begin to dance and sing. The music triggers the memory as well as other parts of the brain so that the patients can remember, communicate, and feel joy. This effect can last up to a few hours.

Says Dr. Surel, "During our life we associate pieces of music or songs with personal events and emotions in our life. The combination of the tune of the music and the lyrics helps awaken the memory with the emotions. Listening to familiar music can also calm chaotic brain activity so that the patient can focus on the present moment, and connect with other people. This method is so successful that the Music and Memory organization founded by Dan Cohen specializes in bringing music to hundreds of health care centers that take care of patients with Alzheimer's & Dementia.[34] They believe that music has the power to activate more parts of the brain than any other type of stimulus. No Pill Will Do That!"

Is Music Encoded in our DNA?

Numerous scientific discoveries show that music is deeply related to our DNA. In his book, *The Extraordinary Healing Power of Ordinary Things: Fourteen Natural Steps to Health and Happiness*, Dr. Larry Dossey recounts his experience of the work of the late Dr. Susumo Ohno, one of the world's great geneticists.[35] A life-long lover of music, Dr. Ohno decided to investigate the relationship between music and DNA. Taking samples of DNA, which is made up of nucleotides, from both humans and other species, he created a musical score by stringing it out and assigning certain musical notes to the nucleotides as they appeared. He then gave it to his wife, Midori, who was a professional violinist to play. The recordings were said to be astonishing, and in some cases, indistinguishable from Bach or Mozart.

Stunned by the beauty of the music, Dr. Dossey contacted Dr. Ohno, who sent him cassette tapes of his DNA music. Dossey later played the tapes to a group of AIDS patients who attended a healing conference. Explained Dr. Dossey in a subsequent interview:

This was in the early days of AIDS therapy. At that time there was not an effective medication and these AIDS patients were very sick. Some came in wheelchairs. They very often had these grotesque images of their body as rotting, diseased and doomed. I decided to play the DNA music for them and to let them know that there is another way to image your body. Your DNA has not changed just because you have AIDS. At core, fundamentally, it can be seen as something beautiful and here is a way to image that. I described to them about how the music was made and so on and then I played it for them. They began to weep. Not just people with AIDS but the whole audience was in tears. This was the first positive image that many of these people had of their bodies since being diagnosed with AIDS.

After the music was played, there was this silence where the only sounds from the audience were sobbing. Then one of them said, 'Could you play that again?' So, we did. And by golly the same sort of thing happened all over again. I was stunned by this more than they I think, because it was a great example of a lot of things including the healing power of music. It brought home to me also that we really do have ways now of creating new images of the body, even in the midst of horrible illness.

If you search the web for "DNA Music" today, you will come up with hundreds of sites where you can download samples for free. (One word of caution, though—these downloads may not be of the highest recording quality. To get the full benefit, it's best to buy a CD or download a CD-quality or higher version.)

One website, founded by renowned composer Stuart Mitchell, has taken DNA Music one stage further. Yourdnasong.com claims to be the "first company in the world to express your own DNA code in music." It specializes in isolating your genetic signature and translating its sequence into musical pitch and rhythm. For a reasonably modest sum, you can have your DNA music translated, arranged, and scored for any solo instrument of your choice, and then performed and recorded by a professional artist. If you're looking for a truly original gift for a loved one, you can even have a fully scored orchestral work translated, produced, and arranged by professional composers. The translation of DNA code into music is a lengthy process, but one only has to listen to the different types of musical samples on their website to appreciate that the final productions result in music of great beauty and expression.[36]

To my knowledge, no one has researched whether listening to your own DNA music would be any more beneficial than listening to other music. However, empirical evidence suggests that specific instruments and types of sounds can help ease certain physical, mental, and emotional conditions.

My own research has entailed reading more than 150 books and studying countless websites. I not only learned a great deal about how specific instruments affect various organs, but I've also conducted my own experiments with them. For example, over the years, I have successfully used the flute for liver issues, gout and sciatica, the piano for resetting the autonomic nervous system, water sounds for PTSD, and drumming to increase the immune function.[37]

Some years ago, we had a medical doctor at my Center use a dark field microscope before and after clients had sessions in the light box. We determined that certain types of music did increase the white blood cells following a session. We did not test to see how long it held, but we were able to see that there was greater activity in the white blood cells directly after the session.

The Sound of Your Own Voice

As Larry Dossey points out in his "Living Dialogues" interview with Duncan Campbell, there is evidence that the sound of your own voice can be healing in itself. For example, he says, "medical research shows that humming is effective in treating chronic sinusitis by the concentration of a particular chemical called nitric oxide in the area of the skull around the sinuses, which has the effect of opening up the sinuses." International authority on sound healing and pioneer in the field of harmonics, Jonathan Goldman, agrees with him.

The author of multiple best-selling books on sound healing and frequencies, Jonathan Goldman's latest book, written with his wife Andi, explores the science behind sound healing. *The Humming Effect: Sound Healing for Health and Happiness* examines how self-created sounds like humming can literally rearrange molecular structure. Humming, say the Goldmans, is one of the simplest and yet most profound sounds we can make. Research has shown it to be much more than a self-soothing sound. Humming affects us on a physical level. It reduces stress, induces calmness, and enhances sleep. It also lowers heart rate and blood pressure, and produces powerful neurochemicals such as oxytocin, which is known as the "love" hormone. Humming not only helps with blood pressure but also increases lymphatic circulation and melatonin production, releases endorphins, creates new neural pathways in the brain, and releases nitric oxide, a neurotransmitter fundamental to health and well-being.[38]

To understand how humming, or any other sound or vibration affects us on a physical level, let's look at the study of cymatics, which demonstrates how sound and vibration create form, and how sound is experienced by our bodies.

Cymatics – the Study of Sound and Vibration

Cymatics is the study of sound and vibration made visible.[39] The term "Cymatics" comes from the Greek word for waveform because sound travels as a wave. It was coined by Swiss physician, artist, and natural scientist Professor Hans Jenny. Jenny found that when sound waves are passed through various kinds of malleable matter, such as water, paste, sand, and plastic, it causes geometric patterns to form. But Jenny wasn't the first person to investigate the power of sound to create forms.

Throughout history, there have been people who have observed and investigated the unique ability sound vibrations have to affect and shape different substances.

In the 15th Century, Leonardo Da Vinci wrote: "I say then that when a table is struck in different places the dust that is upon it is reduced to various shapes of mounds and tiny hillocks. The dust descends from the hypotenuse of these hillocks, enters beneath their base and raises itself again around the axis of the point of the hillock."

In the 16th Century, the Italian philosopher, astronomer, and mathematician, Galileo Galilei, who made fundamental contributions to the sciences of motion, astronomy, and strength of materials as well as the development of the scientific method, described scraping a brass plate with a chisel and noticing a "long row of fine streaks, parallel and equidistant from one another," which was presumed to be caused by the brass filings dancing on the surface of the plate.[40]

In July of 1680, an English architect, polymath, and natural philosopher named Robert Hooke ran a bow along the edge of a glass plate covered with flour and saw nodal patterns emerge.

In the 18th Century, the German musician and physicist Ernst Chladni, who some call "the father of acoustics," noticed that the modes of vibration of a membrane or a plate can be observed by sprinkling the vibrating surface with fine dust such as powder, flour, or fine sand. A century later, the English chemist and physicist, Michael Faraday, recorded many experiments of his studies on how vibration affects water, oil, and fine grains.

In the 20th Century, a German researcher and photographer, Alexander Lauterwasser, influenced by the work of Hans Jenny, photographed the patterns on the surface of water set into motion by the sound of pure sine waves, vocal music, and music by Beethoven. Lauterwasser's 2002 *Wasser Klang Bilder (Water Sound Images)* is claimed to set new standards in cymatic imagery.[41]

Dolphins, Sounds, and Cymatics

In researching this segment on Cymatics, I came across some interesting information about how researchers in Great Britain and the United States have imaged the first high definition imprints that dolphin sounds make in water.

Joan Ocean, M.S., is respected as one of the nation's leading researchers in the field of human-dolphin communication. She is a co-founder with artist Jean-Luc Bozzoli of Dolphin Connection International, an organization that explores the advancement of human consciousness, biophysics, healing, and spirituality. Inspired by a meeting in the 1970s with scientific visionary and explorer, John C. Lilly, M.D., whose work with dolphins and whales provided the basis for the movie *Day of the Dolphin*, and stimulated the enactment of the Marine Mammal Protection Act, Joan Ocean began to develop an unexpected relationship with dolphins who began to communicate with her through meditation and expanded consciousness. After meeting Jean-Luc Bozzoli and experiencing his dolphin-inspired, multi-media art presentation, she began swimming with cetaceans in oceans and rivers in many countries. When a California Grey whale came close to the shores of British Columbia and looked directly into her eyes, Ocean experienced a communication between herself and the whale that changed her life forever.[42]

Ocean says she experiences the gentle communication of the dolphins and whales as sound holography, a language that intensifies physical senses, bypasses rational-cognitive paradigms, resonates directly with our cellular intelligence, and awakens multiple levels of perception and consciousness. Here is how she explains it on her website:

"When the dolphins communicate with me, they send acoustic images through the ocean water (salt water). I hear some of their multi-toned sounds and I receive these images into the cells of my body. Is it being received in my brain? In my mind? In my pineal gland? My heart? Or are their images sent to me and received in the cellular DNA of my entire body? I cannot tell for sure and look forward to learning more about our communication process. But meanwhile, I am receiving this information from them when I am in tel-empathic contact with the dolphins... Which means I am feeling empathy toward them and my feelings of love from my heart are activated (tel-empathy). This vibration that I send out with genuine feelings of love for them, appears to be the conduit to receive their transmissions. It is a frequency that they can receive and send back to me.... And to anyone who is peacefully and lovingly in contact with them in the salt water."

Joan Ocean's research in the field of human-dolphin interactions is shared in two best-selling books, *Dolphin Connection: Interdimensional Ways of Living* and *Dolphins into the Future,* which have been published in multiple languages. She also shared this at the Power of Sound Conference, which she convened in Hawaii in 1996.

While the idea of communicating "holographically" with dolphins may sound a bit far-fetched, the following information from a 2013 press release published on several websites, including Joan Ocean's, provides greater insight into the power of sound. It also underscores much of what I have shared so far about Cymatics, frequency, subtle energy, and telepathic communication about what is happening when we "pick up" or "receive" information from those around us:

In an important breakthrough in deciphering dolphin language, researchers in Great Britain and the United States have imaged the first high definition imprints that dolphin sounds make in water.

The key to this technique is the CymaScope, an instrument that reveals detailed structures within sounds, allowing their architecture to be studied pictorially. Using high definition audio recordings of dolphins, the research team, headed by English acoustics engineer, John Stuart Reid and Florida-based dolphin researcher, Jack Kassewitz, has been able to image, for the first time, the imprint that a dolphin sound makes in water. The resulting "CymaGlyphs," as they have been named, are reproducible patterns that are expected to form the basis of a lexicon of dolphin language, each pattern representing a dolphin "picture word."

Certain sounds made by dolphins have long been suspected to represent language but the complexity of the sounds has made their analysis difficult. Previous techniques, using the spectrograph, display cetacean (dolphins, whales and porpoises) sounds only as graphs of frequency and amplitude. The CymaScope captures actual sound vibrations imprinted in the dolphin's natural environment—water, revealing the intricate visual details of dolphin sounds for the first time.

Within the field of cetacean research, theory states that dolphins have evolved the ability to translate dimensional information from their echolocation sonic beam. The CymaScope has the ability to visualize dimensional structure within sound. CymaGlyph patterns may resemble what the creatures perceive from their own returning sound beams and from the sound beams of other dolphins.

Reid said that the technique has similarities to deciphering Egyptian hieroglyphs. "Jean-Francois Champollion and Thomas Young used the Rosetta Stone to discover key elements of the primer that allowed the Egyptian language to be deciphered. The CymaGlyphs produced on the CymaScope can be likened to the hieroglyphs of the Rosetta Stone. Now that dolphin chirps, click-trains and whistles can be converted into CymaGlyphs, we have an important tool for deciphering their meaning."

Kassewitz, of the Florida-based dolphin communication research project SpeakDolphin.com said, "There is strong evidence that dolphins are able to 'see' with sound, much like humans use ultrasound to see an unborn child in the mother's womb. The CymaScope provides our first glimpse into what the dolphins might be 'seeing' with their sounds."

The team has recognized that sound does not travel in waves, as is popularly believed, but in expanding holographic bubbles and beams. The holographic aspect stems from the physics theory that even a single molecule of air or water carries all the information that describes the qualities and intensity of a given sound. At frequencies audible to humans (20 Hertz to 20,000 Hertz) the sound-bubble form dominates; above 20,000 Hertz the shape of sound becomes increasingly beam shaped, similar to a lighthouse beam in appearance.

Reid explained their novel sound imaging technique: "Whenever sound bubbles or beams interact with a membrane, the sound vibrations imprint onto its surface and form a CymaGlyph, a repeatable pattern of energy. The CymaScope employs the surface tension of water as a membrane because water reacts quickly and is able to reveal intricate architectures within the sound form. These fine details can be captured on camera."

Dr. Horace Dobbs, a leading authority on dolphin-assisted therapy, has joined the team as consultant. "I have long held the belief that the dolphin brain, comparable in size with our own, has specialized in processing auditory data in much the same way that the human brain has specialized in processing visual data. Nature tends not to evolve brain mass without a need, so we must ask ourselves what dolphins do with all that brain capacity. The answer appears to lie in the development of brain systems that require huge auditory processing power. There is growing evidence that dolphins can take a sonic 'snap shot' of an object and send it to other dolphins, using sound as the transmission medium. We can therefore hypothesize that the dolphin's primary method of communication is picture based. Thus, the picture-based imaging method, employed by Reid and Kassewitz, seems entirely plausible."[43]

How Sound Affects Our Brains, Our Emotions, and Our Consciousness

Sound uses entrainment to facilitate shifts in our brainwave state. Entrainment synchronizes our brainwaves by providing a stable rhythm or frequency for them to attune to. When instruments such as tuning forks, gongs, crystal bowls, bells, or drums are used on or near our body, our cells begin to vibrate at the same frequency of the sounds they hear and feel. Just as sound waves are used to break down solid gallstones into more easily dissolvable pieces, sound healing uses the frequencies of various instruments to create sound waves that help down-shift our brainwaves. They can take us from our normal waking consciousness (the beta state) to a more relaxed state of consciousness (alpha), to theta, which is the state achieved in deep meditation, and even all the way down to delta, which is what we are in when we are sleeping. This is where healing occurs.

Diane Mandle is Certified in Tibetan Bowl Sound Healing through the State of California and Sacred Sound Workshops. She maintains a private practice offering an integrated system for healing, which includes sound and polarity therapy, toning, and visualization. She conducts educational presentations, keynotes and Harmonic Sound concerts nationwide on healing with Himalayan bowls. In an article published on *The Healer's Journal* website in 2013, Diane Mandle outlined her understanding of how the sounds generated by such instruments as the Tibetan bowls affect our health:

A vital step in the healing process is that of establishing resonance with the condition in question. Most people resist their condition. You cannot release that which you do not own. Sound is the train that helps us get to healing. How? We now know that different pulses stimulate different brainwave centers. We also know that we can create brainwave entrainment through a process of sympathetic resonance and that we normally entrain or fall into vibrational step to the strongest vibrations in our immediate environment.

Our body is a perfect transmitter of vibration, being 70 percent water. Further, nerve bundles in our spine transmit vibrational sensory data to brain stem and limbic system (our emotional processing center). Placing bowls directly on the body significantly increases their effectiveness. The bowls vibrate at the frequency of perfection, otherwise known as the Sanskrit mantra AUM. They create harmonic overtones in which each note contains all other notes and none is a separate entity on its own. Their sound entrains us into health by entraining our energetic system to resonate with them in their perfection. In the universe every dissonant chord tends toward becoming a harmony.

And that's what they help our bodies to do. The harmonic resonance of the bowls literally pulls us back into a more universal energetic flow. They effectively transmit their soothing and peaceful vibrations through our 70 percent water body in a way that affects our entire nervous and immune system and initiates the relaxation response bringing us into a Theta brainwave state (waking dream state that is home to creativity, inspiration, intuition and where we can let go of our ego boundaries, of our consciousness of our physical state and connect with the non-physical, non-dualistic).

The sound vibrations of the bowls naturally balance our right and left brain and with repetition in conjunction with visualization can hold us in the Theta state for longer and longer periods of time. The vibrational sound from the Himalayan bowls initializes our parasympathetic nervous system and helps to raise the disease fighting immune cells while also reducing our stress response and creating cardio respiratory synchrony (the synchronized flow of our brain, respiratory and heart rate waves). Our capacity to heal from any illness is predicated on our body's ability to achieve cardio-respiratory synchrony and this is exactly what is achieved by listening to the bowls. When they are placed directly on your body, as in a private session, then the healing potential is greatly increased because you are receiving the vibrations in your muscles and organs in addition to hearing them."[44] ***

The Therapeutic Benefits of Music

Scientific studies abound that demonstrate the effects of music on our health. Didgeridoo teacher and performer, AJ Block, has spent years studying music traditions from all over the world. In an article on the Didge Project website, Block says: "Doctors are now prescribing music therapy for heart ailments, brain dysfunction, learning disabilities, depression, PTSD, Alzheimer's, childhood development, and so much more."

*** After conducting intensive research into different types of meditational music, frequency ranges, and instrument tones, I have concluded that the body heals best when it heals naturally, as opposed to being *forced* into balance. Thus, while there are many reported benefits to brain entrainment and binaural beats, I personally am not a fan of any music or modality that claims to *make* the body do something.

Here are a few examples of what Block refers to:

- **Music Helps Control Blood Pressure and Heart-Related Disorders**
  According to The Cardiovascular Society of Great Britain, listening to certain music with a repetitive rhythm for at least ten seconds can lead to a decrease in blood pressure and a reduced heart rate. Certain classical compositions, if matched with a human body's rhythm, can be therapeutically used to keep the heart under control.

- **Listening and Playing Music Helps Treat Stress and Depression**
  A study at McGill University in Canada shared in *Psychology Today* reports that listening to agreeable music encourages the production of beneficial brain chemicals, specifically the "feel good" hormone known as dopamine, which is an integral part of the brain's pleasure enhancing system.

- **Adults Who Play Music Produce Higher Levels of Human Growth Hormone (HGH).**
  According to Web MD, HGH is a necessary hormone for regulating body composition, body fluids, muscle and bone growth, sugar and fat metabolism, and possibly heart function.

- **Music Therapy Helps Treat Alzheimer's Disease**
  According to studies done in partnership with the Alzheimer's Foundation of America, "When used responsibly, music can shift mood, manage stress-induced agitation, stimulate positive interactions, facilitate cognitive function, and coordinate motor movements."

- **Studying Music Boosts Academic Achievement in High Schoolers**
  UCLA professor James S. Catterall analyzed the academic achievement of 6,500 low-income students and found that early exposure to music increases the plasticity of the brain in such a way that it responds readily to learning, changing and growing.

- **Music Therapy Helps Relieve PTSD symptoms**
  The U.S. Department of Veterans Affairs shared a study in which veterans experiencing Post Traumatic Stress Disorder (PTSD) experienced relief by learning to play guitar.

- **Studying Music Boosts Brain Development in Young Children**
  A research-based study undertaken at the University of Liverpool in the field of neuroscience shows that even half an hour of musical training is sufficient to increase the flow of blood in the brain's left hemisphere, resulting in higher levels of early childhood development.

- **Listening to Music Helps Improve Sleep**
  According to The Center for Cardiovascular Disease in China, listening to music before and during sleep greatly aids people who suffer from both acute and chronic sleep disorders, which include everything from stress and anxiety to insomnia.

- **Playing Didgeridoo Helps Treat Sleep Apnea**
  A study published in the British Medical Journal shows that people suffering from sleep apnea can find relief by practicing the Australian wind-instrument known as the didgeridoo.[45]

This is only a small sample of the research that is shining a light on the therapeutic benefits of Sound and Music Healing and Therapy. Thanks to the pioneering work of Sound Healing experts such as Jonathan Beaulieu,[46] and Barry Goldstein,[47] and the popularity of books such as Don Campbell's *The Mozart Effect*,[48] Oliver Sacks' *Musicophilia*,[49] Eileen Day McKusick's *Tuning the Human Biofield*,[50] Dr. Mitchell Gaynor's *Sounds of Healing*,[51] and Daniel J Levitin's *This is Your Brain on Music*,[52] plus numerous others, these disciplines, which used to be dismissed as "fringe" therapies, are now taking what I, for one, consider to be their rightful place in the vanguard of the future of medicine, which is really going back to the way music was used in the past.

The Latest Research – Shattering Cancer with Resonant Frequencies

Anthony Holland is an associate professor and director of Music Technology at Skidmore College. His work with resonant frequencies led to the opening of a cancer lab to test what would happen to cancer cells when they were blasted with certain sound waves. Holland discovered that cancers, including leukemia, uterine cancer, and breast cancer, and even MRSA (the antibiotic-resistant strain of bacteria that's responsible for numerous deaths) are easily destroyed at frequencies between 100,000 Hz and 300,000 Hz. You can watch this happening in the video of his 2013 TEDX talk on YouTube.[53]

How Music is Experienced by Your Body

Dame Evelyn Glennie is a Scottish virtuoso multi-percussionist who performs internationally with a wide variety of orchestras and contemporary musicians. Dame Glennie gives 100 concerts a year as well as master classes and "music in schools" performances. She was featured on Icelandic singer Björk's album *Telegram,* performing the duet "My Spine," and has collaborated with many other musicians including former Genesis guitarist Steve Hackett, Bobby McFerrin, and Mark Knopfler, lead guitarist and lead singer for the band Dire Straits.

Aside from her many accomplishments, there is another factor that marks Evelyn Glennie as someone out of the ordinary. She has been profoundly deaf since the age of twelve, having started to lose her hearing from the age of eight. But clearly, this has never inhibited her ability to perform at an international level.

How does she do it? Dame Evelyn taught herself to hear with parts of her body other than her ears. She regularly plays barefoot during both live performances and studio records so she can *feel* the pitches and rhythms of her fellow musicians. When performing, she knows what the pitch is based on where she feels it resonating in her body.

In an essay she published on hearing, Dame Evelyn explained why she doesn't believe that what she does is extraordinary:

> Deafness is poorly understood in general. For instance, there is a common misconception that deaf people live in a world of silence. To understand the nature of deafness, first one has to understand the nature of hearing.

Hearing is basically a specialized form of touch. Sound is simply vibrating air which the ear picks up and converts to electrical signals, which are then interpreted by the brain. The sense of hearing is not the only sense that can do this, touch can do this too. If you are standing by the road and a large truck goes by, do you hear or feel the vibration? The answer is both. With very low frequency vibration the ear starts becoming inefficient and the rest of the body's sense of touch starts to take over. For some reason, we tend to make a distinction between hearing a sound and feeling a vibration, in reality they are the same thing. It is interesting to note that in the Italian language this distinction does not exist. The verb "sentire" means to hear, and the same verb in the reflexive form "sentirsi" means to feel. Deafness does not mean that you can't hear, only that there is something wrong with the ears. Even someone who is totally deaf can still hear/feel sounds.

If we can all feel low-frequency vibrations why can't we feel higher vibrations? It is my belief that we can, it's just that as the frequency gets higher and our ears become more efficient, they drown out the subtler sense of "feeling" the vibrations.

Dame Evelyn Glennie discusses how she feels music in different parts of her body in her TED talk, "How to Truly Listen" published in 2003.[54]

What's the Difference Between Sound Healing and Music Therapy?

The differences between Sound Healing and Music Therapy are subtle but distinct. While both may use instruments or the voice to facilitate healing, the intent of sound healing is to find and produce specific frequencies, which may be unique to the individual, that can then be directed internally to facilitate healing. Whether through an intricate musical passage or with a single toned note, the focus is on influencing sound's energy to facilitate change in a person and/or environment.

Music Therapy is an established health profession in which music is used within a therapeutic relationship to address a person's physical, emotional, cognitive, and social needs. It bases its protocols on what is known about music's structure and rhythm to actively engage a client in music-making to address a specific health outcome. After assessing the strengths and individual needs of a client, the qualified music therapist provides the indicated treatment, including creating, singing, moving to, and/or listening to music. In other words, Music Therapy is the clinical and evidence-based use of music interventions to accomplish individualized goals within a therapeutic relationship by a credentialed professional who has completed an approved music therapy program.

Alfred A. Tomatis was a French otolaryngologist and inventor who received his Doctorate in Medicine from the Paris School of Medicine. His theories of hearing and listening are known as the Tomatis Method or Audio-Psycho-Phonology (APP). According to Dr. Tomatis, who was widely considered to be the "grandfather of modern psychoacoustics," sound is a "nutrient for the nervous system." [55] Inspired by research into the therapeutic benefits of sound and music, many well-known composers and musicians have been broadening their own repertoire to include compositions that are specifically geared toward healing.

Music and Sound as Medical Prescriptions

Barry Goldstein is a Grammy-award winning producer, composer and musician whose musical experience spans many styles and genres from co-producing the Grammy award-winning track "69 Freedom Special" with Les Paul for Best Rock Instrumental in 2005, to providing ambient music for Shirley MacLaine.[56] He has composed and produced for TV, film, and top ten recording artists. As an artist, he reached the Billboard top ten albums on the New Age Charts with author Neale Donald Walsch. He has composed and produced music for New York Times best-selling authors, Dr. Daniel Amen, Dr. Joe Dispenza, Gregg Braden, and Anita Moorjani. And he has also written articles and facilitates workshops on utilizing music, sound, and vibration in the healing process.

Goldstein's book *The Secret Language of the Heart: How to Use Music, Sound and Vibration as Tools for Healing and Transformation*, shares how every one of us—the musical and the non-musical alike—can harness the power of music to alleviate specific illnesses, reverse negative mindsets and attitudes, dissolve creative blocks and improve overall health. It has been praised by several pioneers in the medical arena, including Dr. Daniel Amen, Dr. Norman Shealy, Dr. Stephen Sinatra, and Dr. James Oschman. Barry Goldstein's music, which is used in hospitals, hospices, cancer centers, and medical practices, is now being studied by researchers from major universities to determine health benefits.

Together with his wife, Dr. Donese Worden, an internationally renowned award-winning Naturopathic Physician, Goldstein has now created a "Musical and Medical Prescriptions for Health" Program, which they present at medical conferences and inspirational forums.[57] Passionate about sharing the new science and research documenting the benefits of music, chanting, and mantra, as well as the true potential of music in integrative medical settings, the duo's goal is to educate the medical community. As Goldstein declares on his website: "Music as medicine is gaining attention in the medical world as we begin to uncover the possibilities of prescribing low cost, non-invasive treatment utilizing specific music for specific conditions."

Yuval Ron is another world-renowned musician and composer whose work is now incorporating "Music as Medicine." An educator, peace activist, lecturer, and record producer, he has composed music for the Oscar-winning film, *West Bank Story*. He's also performed for the Dalai Lama and collaborated with Sufi leaders, Zen Buddhist priests, visual artists, choreographers, and neuroscientists.[58]

When Yuval met Dr. Richard Gold while teaching at the Esalen Institute in California, neither had any idea that their chance encounter would result in profound collaborations to create new music for healing and well-being that incorporate the power of music, sound, and sacred chants.

Dr. Richard Gold is a pioneering integrative health practitioner and licensed acupuncturist with a doctorate in psychology. In addition to co-founding the Pacific College of Oriental Medicine, he has conducted extensive study in neuroscience and the effects of sound and meditation on the brain.[59] Together, Yuval Ron and Dr. Gold founded the sound healing company Metta Mindfulness Music. Their aim is beautifully summarized in their mission statement: to "create beautiful original music that is informed by ancient wisdom traditions and the most current advances in neuroscience and music therapy to enhance health, mental equanimity and the daily expression of loving kindness." Their Metta Music Medicine series is based on the wisdom of traditional Chinese medicine five-element theory, and recent advances in modern neuroscience. It features brain entrainment music for many ailments, including relieving stress, sleeplessness, indigestion, belly ache, breathlessness, and breathing. Their other healing music CDs include a Dosha Music series, which takes listeners on an aural journey through the Doshas of Ayurvedic Medicine, and a Medicine for the Soul album called "Voyage Through the Chakras," which combines guided meditations, mantras, and embedded subliminal affirmations.[60]

In my role as producer of the Elvis movie, I'd had to learn about music rights and licenses, trademarks, copyrights, and many other laws and measures for protecting the intellectual property rights of artists and inventors. Working with Fred, I'd had reservations about the way he managed his music selections for the light box. It bothered me that the CD's he used contained generic labels with numbers, such as Disc 1 or Disc 2, instead of crediting the official title and name of the composer. He seemed to be very cagey about sharing the origins of some of the selections he used. To me, it gave a false impression, and I had often wondered whether Fred wanted clients to think that the music was his own creation.

With this in mind, the first thing I did after developing the Harmonic Egg was to call the American Society of Composers, Authors, and Publishers (ASCAP). ASCAP is an American non-profit, performance-rights organization that protects its members' musical copyrights by monitoring public performances of their music and compensating them accordingly. ASCAP duly sent me a contract, requiring me to pay an annual fee for the right to play professional music in the Harmonic Egg.

In the interim, I've reached out to many music artists about creating music explicitly for the Egg. My dream was to find musicians who have a sufficiently high degree of consciousness and integrity to become part of the energy of the Egg. Despite some enjoyable conversations, however, I drew a blank. Some composers were too busy to create something new. Others' fees exceeded my budget.

At least, that's what I thought at the time. Little did I know that the Universe was about to deliver me another lesson in synchronicity and divine timing. Because I then met my co-writer and editor, Sandie Sedgbeer, who has more strings to her bow (pun most definitely intended) than just word-smithing and publishing. As it transpired, Sandie is a seasoned broadcaster and talk TV/radio show host. Her show, What Is Going Om, is the flagship radio show for OMTimes Magazine's radio network. And her guests are new thought authors, speakers, teachers, and conscious creators working at the frontiers of science and spirituality.[61]

A believer in synchronicity, Sandie laughed when I shared my dream. "Well, if you're looking for highly conscious musicians and composers," she said. "You have to meet two men I recently interviewed who are working at the leading edge of healing music."

Cue my introduction to Yuval Ron and Dr. Richard Gold. (Truly, you can't make this stuff up!)

After checking into Yuval's and Richard's individual backgrounds and accomplishments, I had some doubts about their approachability. But I needn't have worried. Yuval and Richard were both immensely likable, down-to-earth, and blessedly easy to work with. I shared my observations about the five primary causes of disease, and the different instruments and colors that I'd noted as having effects on the well-being of my clients. They were excited by the possibilities of creating custom-made music for the Harmonic Egg to address the five causes I had identified. We agreed that I would instruct Yuval on the best instruments to use. Yuval would then use his expertise to mix and master specific tracks and music for each cause. And with the assistance of Richard and his Chinese medicine expertise, we would create instructions on how to use the music, detailing the organs and elements with which each piece of music corresponded.

After spending a few months collaborating on the music, I listened to each track inside the Egg. Although the process was time-consuming, it was also immensely rewarding to finally have a unique, six-volume series of "Harmonic Egg Wellness Tracks." This series utilizes the tones and frequencies of specific instruments to augment the healing experience of anyone using the Harmonic Egg.

Titles include "Reduce Inflammation," "Stress-Less," "Boost Immunity," "Liver Remedy," "Heavy Metal Detox," and "Kid's Sanctuary." I'm proud of them all. And I am especially proud of the Kids Sanctuary album, which was designed for energetically sensitive beings and the autistic community, for whom sounds can sometimes be challenging or over-stimulating. Kids Sanctuary incorporates the sounds of just flute, water, and birds to soothe and calm the senses. (Adults find it incredibly soothing and restful too.)[62]

The icing on this incredible cake is that Yuval, Richard, and I have become good friends. And we intend to collaborate on another track for the Frequency of Love, which is the highest vibration of all. So, stay tuned, we anticipate the seventh Harmonic Wellness Track will make its appearance in the Spring of 2020. What's exciting to me is that Yuval plans to coach every musician who plays on the track to hold the intention of love throughout the entire recording process! I believe there will be no other musical track as unique as this piece. We will be incorporating some very unique ideas that will be written up and shared with the track.

Of course, listening to the Harmonic Egg Wellness tracks cannot compare to the whole-body experience of being immersed in the resonant frequencies created by the combination of sacred geometry, sound, light, and color waves of the Harmonic Egg. But it does provide a relaxing way to stay anchored after a session, as well as a small taste of the Harmonic Egg.

Best of all was that Yuval and Richard both had their own amazing experiences in the Harmonic Egg, which you can read about in Part III.

In today's fast-paced, technology-driven world where our minds and bodies are continually being assaulted by lower-frequency vibrations of stress, anger, negativity, fear, and hard to avoid electromagnetic frequencies and pollution, it's exciting to see the following prediction, made in the last century by America's most famous clairvoyant, Edgar Cayce, finally being realized. In more ways than one, it truly is music to our ears.

"Sound will be the medicine of the future."
— EDGAR CAYCE

CHAPTER NINE

Sacred Geometry & Light

When Dan Brown's book, *The Da Vinci Code*, hit the bestseller lists, millions of readers around the world became familiar with an aspect of geometry not taught in schools. One that demonstrates how geometric models can help us understand the evolution of consciousness and the divine nature of human beings and the physical world.

Throughout history, architects and temple builders have relied on magic numbers to shape sacred spaces. Astronomers have used geometry to calculate holy seasons, and philosophers have observed the harmony of the universe in the numerical properties of music. The knowledge of magical symbols and sacred geometry was revered and preserved by many ancient civilizations, including those in Mesopotamia, Egypt, India, and Greece. In ancient times, magical symbols and geometry worked together as keys to understanding nature and the philosophical meaning of existence. By showing how the discoveries of mathematics are manifested over and over again in biology and physics, and how they have inspired the greatest works of art, sacred geometry reveals the universal principles that link us to the infinite.

The geometric models of sacred geometry are said to mirror our consciousness. According to the Seed of Life Institute, (SOLi), founded by seminar leaders, authors, and spiritual teachers Ronald Holt and Lyssa Royal Holt, whose **SOLi School** offers classes on spiritual growth and awakening:

Just as our bodies are expressions of our consciousness in a physical form, the physical geometric forms are representations of the original geometry of light that exists beyond the physical level. On this original level beyond the physical, geometric forms fluidly transition into each other, representing how our consciousness continuously transcends and moves into higher and higher states of evolution.

The key element that ties the geometry together is that of the spiral, creating a tree of transcendent geometries that represent our true infinite nature. For example, the ancient Flower of Life pattern that has been found in temples, burial sites, and sacred locations around the world, which is shown often in the works of Leonardo Da Vinci, has a unique quality. Within this pattern, all the geometric forms known in creation can be found. Thus, the Flower of Life symbol is known as a symbol of creation that clearly expresses the unity of all "separate" objects in creation.[63]

Leonardo Da Vinci was just one of many ancients who studied sacred geometry and its connection to the creation of physical reality and consciousness. Freemasons and hermeticists of old are said to have believed that the universe is the material expression of a hidden reality; an invisible blueprint, created by God, who they also referred to as "the Great Architect of the Universe." They believed that sacred geometry is the key to revealing that which is concealed—i.e., that these fundamental geometric relations, manifested through form, pattern, and number, form the very basis of harmony.

The Christian theologian, St. Augustine, held both Pythagoras and Plato in high regard. He grasped the significance of geometric form, pattern and proportion, and their representation through numerical symbolism, when he made the statements: *"Numbers are the thoughts of God,"* and *"The construction of the physical and moral world alike is based on eternal numbers."*

Galileo also demonstrated his understanding of this geometrical/ numerical dimension of reality when he declared that *"Mathematics is the alphabet with which God has written the universe."* And again, as did Johannes Kepler when he stated that *"Geometry existed before the Creation. It is co-eternal with the mind of God…Geometry provided God with a model for the Creation."*

Sacred geometry was very important in the time of the Renaissance, which spanned the 14th to 17th centuries. This is especially evident when we look back at cities such as Florence, which rose to prominence in the time of the Renaissance. Influenced by the styles and wisdom of ancient Greece and Rome, Renaissance philosophers, politicians, writers, artists, and architects began to adopt a more holistic ethic. One that incorporated religion, art, science, and esoteric topics such as sacred geometry. Hence, geometric proportions such as the Golden Mean and the Flower of Life were hidden in many famous paintings, buildings, and sculptures of that time.

Three great masters of that period are all known to have used sacred geometry in their famous works. Raffaello Sanzio da Urbino, the great

Italian painter and architect whose work is so famous he is simply known as Raphael, was a student and practitioner of sacred geometry.[64] He employed the Golden Ratio in works such as The School of Athens, a great fresco on the Stanze di Raffaello, in the Vatican's Apostolic Palace. Among the many figures depicted in this fresco are Aristotle, Heraclitus, Socrates, and Pythagoras, who, of course, plays a significant role in the history of sacred geometry. And as we learned in the *Da Vinci Code*, in which the hero, Robert Langdon was a cryptologist (someone who studies the techniques of secret symbols, ciphers, and codes), Leonardo Da Vinci incorporated numerous examples of sacred geometry in his works too, including The Last Supper and the Mona Lisa, which shows strong evidence that he used the Golden Ratio. And then there is Michelangelo, who experts say used the Golden Ratio more than two dozen times in painting the Vatican's Sistine Chapel.

When I was 'downloading' information about the elements necessary to incorporate in the Harmonic Egg, I wasn't entirely surprised when sacred geometry was among them. I had already studied the subject somewhat and was familiar with the work of Drunvalo Melchizedek, the Flower of Life, and geometric shapes in nature.[65] When I researched the subject more deeply, however, it became evident that sacred geometry plays a pivotal role in intertwining with the frequencies of light, color, sound, and frequency to create the perfect space for healing to occur.

One site that I found especially fascinating is Phidle.com, which sells conscious clothing and accessories inspired by sacred geometry and ancient symbolism. What I like about this site is that it's not just about selling. It goes way beyond that by offering its customers an incredible value-added benefit with intelligent, well-written articles on the science and history of sacred geometry, ancient symbolism, and the mathematics of nature. If you're interested in learning more about these important topics, I urge you to check out the articles under their Sacred Stories tab.[66]

Sacred Geometry and Our DNA

As discussed in Chapter Seven, the science of epigenetics shows that we have more power over shaping how our DNA expresses itself than we previously thought. And our emotions, beliefs, and actions can "turn on" and "turn off" specific components in our DNA that affect our health. When researchers began conducting experiments to determine just how these "on" and "off" switches are structured, they found that our DNA is actually designed around distinct sets of mathematical symmetries. That's right, Phi (pronounced, "Fi"), the Fibonacci Sequence, and fractal patterns are all encoded in our very DNA.

This discovery was borne out in an abstract entitled *Deciphering Hidden DNA Meta-Codes - The Great Unification & Master Code of Biology,* which stated:

> Studies of our DNA structure seem to indicate that we are specifically designed using the Universal language of cohesive proportions. Just as irrational fractal patterns are formed on leaves to allow for optimal sunlight and rainwater to reach both upper and lower branches, so too does our DNA blueprint use sacred geometric patterns to help us form advantageous processes of healthy self-organization. [67]

Let There be Light!

Light is essential to our health and well-being. It nourishes the body and stimulates and supports our important endocrine system, organs, and immune system. Light enters our body through our eyes and also via the skin, our energy field and our chakras. The visible spectrum is the portion of the electromagnetic spectrum that is visible to our eyes. Electromagnetic radiation in this range of wavelengths is called visible light or just light. The visible spectrum and infrared (IR) and ultraviolet (UV) light are essential for the body to maintain optimal health. It has been shown that two hours of indirect sunlight or 30 minutes of direct sunlight every day creates healthier bodies and emotional well-being. Unfortunately, we have become a society that tends to spend long periods indoors bathed in artificial lighting.

When we're outdoors, we protect our eyes from the sun with darkened glasses or contact lenses, and we protect our bodies from its UV rays with sunscreen or UV ray-blocking clothing. But when we block UV rays in this manner, we also block some portion of the spectrum of light, which starves a part of our body.

Dr. Jacob Israel Liberman is a pioneer in the fields of light, vision, and consciousness who has a remarkable story. Originally trained as an optometrist and vision scientist, his life dramatically changed in 1976 when the miraculous healing of his own eyesight led him to a deeper understanding of light and the science of life. Today, he is an internationally respected public speaker and a board member of the International Light Association.[68]

Dr. Liberman is the author of *Luminous Life: How the Science of Life Unlocks the Art of Living*, which integrates 40 years of research, practice, and direct experience. In it, Dr. Liberman writes about treating cancer, AIDS, and other illnesses using color (more on this later) and light, which he calls "an essential nutrient." He uses the term "malillumination" to describe the state in which most of us in the Western world have been living since we moved from predominantly rural life to living in cities.

In 1978, Dr. Liberman wrote in his diary: "It is the concept of time that is the cause of accidents, stress, and physical ailments. We developed this concept to improve our efficiency and control our destiny. Unfortunately, the monster we created is in constant competition with us, and it is winning. If we didn't race against time, we wouldn't have accidents. If we didn't 'think ahead,' our organs wouldn't have to work so hard and break down as often. The clock now controls us." But today, he warns, it is not just our clocks. It's our computers, tablets, phones, the internet, and more.

Jacob Liberman maintains that the human eye is primarily intended for distance vision. But as a result of the widespread use of computers and handheld devices, deteriorating vision is now the world's largest health epidemic and is continuously growing. For example, a 2010 Kaiser Family Foundation report noted that children from 8-18 spend an average of seven hours and thirty-eight minutes a day using entertainment media. The Centers for Disease Control and Prevention report that the diagnosis of ADHD has continued to rise at an alarming rate for more than a decade. And exposure to screen media was associated with attention problems in a sample of 210 college students. But it does not stop there. According to the late Dr. Paul Pearsall, a psycho-neuroimmunologist and New York Times bestselling author, all of us have become media-frenzied and have developed a form of adult attention deficit disorder (AADD).

An Australian study published in *The Lancet* in October 2015 demonstrated that vision worsens in near-sighted children who spend less time outdoors. In China, Taiwan, Japan, Singapore, and South Korea today, up to 90 percent of students are near-sighted. It's claimed that the pressure to perform academically is forcing them to spend most of their time indoors, which is depriving them of the sunlight that allows their eyes to develop.[69] These statistics further confirm a 2009 National Eye Institute study that found an alarming 66 percent increase in the incidence of myopia in the United States since the early 1970s. Based on the results of studies like these, researchers recommend that children spend at least one to two hours per day outdoors to prevent near-sightedness or slow its progression.

The Damaging Effects of Light Pollution

An article on light pollution published on the Natural Energy Hub website states: "All life forms depend on the earth's circadian (day-night) rhythm and have tuned their DNA to work accordingly. Adding light to the environment, which literally turns night into day, has damaging effects on many species of animals including insects, amphibians, birds and reptiles, which use these rhythms to coordinate hunting, rest, reproduction and protection patterns. Plants are not spared from this." The article continues:

> Disturbing our body clocks has caused ill effects on the human body. Many people do not experience complete darkness anymore. Working at night has become normal for a section of society that has become global and does not want to waste a moment of time. Working and living in artificially lighted environments have adverse effects on our organ systems leading to obesity, depression, sleep disorders, diabetes, cancers, and more.
>
> Melatonin a hormone released according to the circadian rhythm of our body has anti-oxidant properties, induces sleep, improves the immune system, controls cholesterol levels, and keep the functioning of important glands such as thyroid, pancreas, ovaries, testes and adrenals at their best. Melatonin production is affected by night time exposure to artificial light.
>
> Blue light that is released from most LEDs used in outdoor lighting, mobile phones, tablets and computers is harmful. The American Medical Association recommends shielding all outdoor lights and using lighting with 3000K color temperature and below. A color temperature app can also be downloaded to make your computer or tablet screen more temperature consistent depending on day or night.
>
> Low temperature light sources are less harmful to the environment and health. They are usually marked warm white sources and are of temperatures below 3000K. This is best used for indoor and outdoor lighting.
>
> Artificial glare causes a reduction in contrast hence reducing vision. This affects aging eyes the most and causes many accidents, as it reduces the ability to detect dangers in time.[70]

The History of Heliotherapy

Sunbathing wasn't always regarded as a health hazard. On the contrary, many ancient cultures believed in the health-promoting properties of the sun. The Egyptians, Babylonians, and Assyrians had sun gardens and gave the sun the status of a god. The Greek physician, Hippocrates, who is widely regarded as the "father of medicine," recommended sunbathing as an effective treatment for several diseases, and regularly used his own large solarium. The ancient Romans had thermae (hot tubs and baths), which were equipped with solaria, and the Roman writer Pliny wrote that "the sun is the best remedy."

Although there's little recorded evidence of sunbathing for several centuries after, heliotherapy, which is the term used to describe the therapeutic use of sunlight or other light wavelengths, started to regain popularity in the late 1800s when it was recommended as a cure for tuberculosis. Since sunlight is not available all the time, however, artificial alternatives were developed that could mimic the sun's beneficial effects. One of the best-known examples is the Finsen Lamp, an ultraviolet lamp invented by physician Niels Ryberg Finsen, which allowed treatment in all seasons. Its greatest success was in the treatment of lupus, for which Finsen was awarded a Nobel prize in 1903.[71]

Why We Need (Some) UV Light

Much is made of the dangers of over-exposing our bodies to the sun, which I am not discounting. However, there also are benefits to the sun that we should not overlook. Vitamin D, which is proving to be even more critical to our health and well-being than initially thought, is produced in the body when the sun's UV rays make contact with our skin. This vitamin helps in the formation of bones, treating rickets, lowering blood pressure, and enhancing our immune system's ability to combat bacterial, viral, and fungal infections. Now that we spend so little time outside in natural light, vitamin D deficiency is again becoming a problem with the Centers for Disease Control and Prevention claiming that more than half of the general population is deficient.

The Earth's atmosphere blocks most of the sun's UV radiation from penetrating through the atmosphere. The small amount that gets through has both positive and negative effects. In addition to activating vitamin D synthesis, UV light is claimed to lower blood pressure, increase heart performance, improve ECG and blood parameters in people suffering from arteriosclerosis, lower cholesterol counts, and promote the production of skin and sex hormones.

Three decades ago, Jacob Liberman challenged the myth that the sun is dangerous to our well-being. He claimed that technological advancements, such as most fluorescent lighting, sunglasses, tanning lotions, and our indoor lifestyles, may be more harmful than helpful. He stresses the importance and curative/health-maintaining value of natural full-spectrum light.

He also cautions that using sunglasses every time we go out artificially filters the light energy entering our eyes, which affects every function of our body. He suggests we spend at least a little time outdoors each day without such protection—even if it's only one or two minutes at first. This will help to build up exposure gradually. We should aim for 20 minutes in total to ensure the minimum daily requirement of light.

Light as Medicine

The International Light Association (ILA) connects researchers, scientists, educators, architects, interior designers, and philosophers who are passionate about learning and applying the latest theories, techniques, and technologies regarding how light and color can promote health, enhance performance and learning and raise consciousness.[72]

Anadi Martel is the president of the ILA. A physicist by training, Martel has been applying his intimate knowledge of electronics to the development of instruments working in novel ways with sound, light, and brainwaves. His Spatial Sound Processors have been used worldwide by professionals in psychoacoustics, multimedia, and cinema. His work has led to patents in the field of light modulation, and recently in LED-based design. According to Martel, we can thank two important studies for bringing light to the forefront of scientific research. The first was understanding how light affects cell metabolism through a process called photo-biomodulation. This was discovered by Russian researcher, Professor Tiina Karu, whose extensive research in the 1990s led to our current understanding of the exact mechanism through which light, especially infrared light or deep-red light, enhances cell metabolism.[73]

The second discovery that changed the whole picture for light was the discovery of what is called the non-visual optic pathway. This is a pathway within the brain that links the retina directly to the hypothalamus, the core of the brain that regulates our whole hormonal balance. This is separate from the visual pathway of the optic nerve, which brings light to the visual processing centers.

Because of these two significant discoveries, thousands of researchers are now exploring light as a powerful healing methodology. Behavioral optometrist, Ray Gottlieb, O.D., Ph.D., has been Dean of the College of Syntonic Optometry (CSO) since 1984. He began his syntonic career in 1975, applying light frequencies for vision problems and has taught and written about clinical and scientific developments in light therapy for nearly 25 years. In 2011, Gottlieb retired and moved to Florida, where he dedicates his time to researching, writing, and lecturing about phototherapy, attention and memory training, presbyopia, eye exercises, and anti-aging. Speaking at the International Light Association (ILA) Conference in 2017, Dr. Gottlieb said:

> I've been passionately interested in the various applications of different types of light for medical purposes. But also for understanding the basic physics, chemistry and biology related to how light works, and what allows it to make such important changes in physiology to heal many different types of maladies.
>
> Light has been used to deal with head injury, with strokes, neurological degeneration problems including Alzheimer's, and Parkinson's. Applications of light have been used for years for skin maladies, for bone healing, spinal injury, visual problems including glaucoma and cataract and macular degeneration. So, there's a great deal of hope that we bring to the idea of light helping physiology and therefore helping medical conditions.
>
> One of the things I find so interesting is, every time they find a new application of light, they discover new aspects of how the physiology and the biology works. Every part of healing has to do with the cell improving itself, rebalancing itself, creating more energy. And some of the discoveries that they're finding with respect to those processes, those functions in the cell, have light more and more playing a very vital role. That's very exciting to me because once we understand more how light actually creates physiological and functional changes, the more we can apply it more directly to various types of problems.

NIR Light Therapy

In October of 2013, the Science Daily website published an exciting press release titled *Light as Medicine? Researchers Explain How.*[74]

Multiple sclerosis (MS) causes progressive paralysis by destroying nerve cells and the spinal cord. It interrupts vision, balance and even thinking.

On a suggestion from a colleague, Jeri-Anne Lyons, an associate professor of biomedical sciences at the University of Wisconsin-Milwaukee (UWM), who studies the role of the immune response in MS, decided to test how the disease responded to a radical therapy -- exposure to a certain wavelength of light called near-infrared (NIR). "Never in a million years did I think it would help," says Lyons. But it *did*. In rodent models, early MS-like symptoms were treated with exposure to NIR light for a week, alternating with a week of no light. The clinical condition of the mice improved.

Professor Janis Eells, who shared the idea with Lyons, had the same initial reaction after she used NIR therapy on rats to treat blindness caused by poisoning, a condition thought to be permanent. Repeating experiments again and again, she found that certain doses of NIR light allowed lab animals to regain their sight.[****]

Scientists have known for years that certain wavelengths of light in certain doses can heal, but they are only now uncovering exactly how it works, thanks in large part to three UWM faculty researchers, including Chukuka S. Enwemeka, dean of UWM's College of Health Sciences who is internationally known for his work in phototherapy.

Enwemeka researches the effects of both NIR and blue light in the visible range on healing wounds. Among his discoveries is that some wavelengths of blue light can clear stubborn infections—even MRSA, the antibiotic-resistant "superbug" form of *Staphylococcus aureus*.

Together, the UWM cluster has found that NIR and blue light repair tissue in dramatically different ways, but both act on the same enzyme in the cell's energy supply center: the mitochondria. The studies have revealed key information about managing the effects of aging and disease.

[****] I have read several industry articles about the dangers of overexposure to infrared light and heat sources to be damaging to the retina, cornea and tissues. I personally believe that ultrasounds can be damaging to babies' tissues and ours as well if we have too many ultrasounds in a short period of time. When technology is used properly it is wonderful, but when it's overused or operators are not trained well, it can be very harmful.[75]

A bodyguard

So how is light accomplishing such wonders? Analyzing the effect the light had on the activities of the animal's genes, Lyons found that molecules that would make the disease worse were weakened after exposure to the light, and the ones responsible for improvement were strengthened. Eells says that certain wavelengths, at a certain intensity, for a certain amount of time, act on the mitochondria and a particular enzyme, cytochrome C oxidase, to stimulate cell repair.

Promising leads

Even more exciting is phototherapy's potential to improve a host of other degenerative diseases. Damaged mitochondria lead to a rise in destructive "free radicals," which play a key role in aging and cancer. "It's why we try to put antioxidants into our diets," says Lyons, "to fight that process." One source of free radicals comes from the inflammation caused by the body's immune response. The researchers have found that after an injury or illness triggers the immune response, NIR light resets the mitochondria so they function normally again.

A similar observation with inflammation occurred in a study on recalcitrant bedsores, she adds. Wounds treated with phototherapy healed two and a half times more quickly than untreated wounds. "Chronic non-healing wounds are 'stuck' in the inflammatory phase of wound healing. The light removes that obstacle," says Eells.

She has been working with Tim Kern at Case Western Reserve in treating an animal model of diabetic retinopathy with NIR light, which has been shown to slow progression and reduce the severity of the condition. Kern hopes to initiate a clinical trial in the near future.

Limited availability

Enwemeka is leading a research effort in Brazil and at UWM that he hopes will ultimately lead to clinical use of NIR and blue light in the U.S. for the treatment of wounds.

In the six years since he was asked to test the effects of blue light on MRSA, he says, research on the topic has picked up. But currently, the U.S. Food and Drug Administration (FDA) has not sanctioned the use of blue light in treating wounds, or NIR light for conditions other than wounds and pain.

Biophotons: The Light in Our Cells

From our skin through to the core of every organ and cell in our body, we are made of light. Light is the language by which our cells speak to one another. The DNA within the center of the nucleus of each of our cells has been shown to emit photons (light). When this light reaches the crystalline structure of the cell wall, it is greatly amplified. The light radiated from the cell naturally congregates with like cells because they share the same frequency (color) of light. These groups of cells form organs and the other structures in our body, each resonating with a specific frequency and color. What this means is that our cells literally are crystallized light.

The amount of research that is currently emerging on the therapeutic uses for light as both therapy and medicine demonstrates that we are in the middle of a revolution in light and frequency medicine. While I would have loved to include more examples of the therapeutic uses of light here, to do so would turn this book into an encyclopedia! Still, I hope I have shared enough to provide sufficient testimony to its phenomenal healing power, to demonstrate why light is such an important feature of the Harmonic Egg, and to explain why combining light and sound can create an even more beneficial healing modality for the future. And if that's not enough, well, there will be more clues in Part III.

"If colors are vibrations of spiritual forces, they should be able to help in healing our deepest and most subtle maladies. Together with music, which is a kindred spiritual force, they form a great hope for therapy of the future."
—Edgar Cayce

I began this section by sharing the research of Dr. Jacob Liberman. I shall end it by sharing a thought-provoking quote from him that hints at an aspect of light that I haven't really covered thus far. But as the following quote reveals, there is so much more to light than we can possibly imagine.

"Eye contact fully activates the parts of the brain that allow us to accurately perceive, process, and interact with others and our environment. When we make eye contact with another person, we literally *exchange our light with them*, which is why we can often sense someone looking at us *before we see them.* Even the brains of individuals who are legally blind get measurably activated when somebody looks at them."

I resonate with Jacob Liberman's work and his assertion that we can heal our eyesight. As I am always telling my clients, if our bones can heal and cuts can seal up by themselves, and our liver can regenerate, why can't our eyes heal? I wore glasses from the age of 19 to 37 when I improved my vision using sound and light. I didn't need glasses again until I had the car accident in November of 2016. I think that part of the downturn in my vision since then was getting the "smart" phone—you know, the phones that make us dumb. Since then, I've noticed a slow decline in my eyesight. I haven't had time to focus on healing my vision again... but I will.

CHAPTER TEN

Frequency, Color
& Numbers

On February 4th, 2019, *Woman's World* magazine carried a cover line that read, "Wow! Instant Color Test Uncovers the Problem Making You Tired!" Inside, a two-page article headlined, "Color healed my broken heart and made my life beautiful again," related the story of Mary Jo Zimmer, who had fallen into a depression after the death of her husband from pancreatic cancer. Somehow, by accident, a book was randomly delivered to Mary Jo's house, which was to change her life in ways she never could have imagined. That book is one with which you will by now be familiar: *Luminous Life* by Dr. Jacob Liberman. Baffled but intrigued, Mary Jo thumbed through the pages thinking, *"I didn't order this… where did it come from?"* As the article by writer Stacey Colino details:

…The book discussed the concept of color homeopathy, which purports that by exposing yourself to specific hues, you can change your emotions, energy and well-being. *Maybe this can help me out of this darkness,* she thought, her heart filling with hope for the first time in months. Excited, Mary Jo contacted Dr. Liberman, and after purchasing his color homeopathy kit, which includes 13 pairs of eyeglasses with different colored lenses, she began working with him through FaceTime.

"All life experiences—both emotional and physical —are a blend of different vibrations," Dr. Liberman explained to Mary Jo. "Colors are the visual representations of these vibrations and the colors we feel uncomfortable with often trigger allergic-like reactions because they are related to unresolved traumas. But by identifying and desensitizing ourselves to those problematic colors, we become comfortable with them again, which helps heal that negative energy and emotion."

After doing a color analysis, Mary Jo expressed discomfort or felt 'allergic' to the colors red and yellow. Dr. Liberman suggested she slowly desensitize herself to these hues by combining them with two shades she liked. He advised Mary Jo to pair the yellow with green (a color she enjoys and that resonates with love and joy) and layer the red with violet (representing selflessness and higher consciousness). She wore the yellow-green lenses, then the red-violet ones, for five to 10 minutes per pair, up to six times a day. Within a matter of days, the effects had begun to kick in. "I feel more emotionally grounded and more whole—it's as though more of me is present," Mary Jo enthused to Dr. Liberman.

Over time, as Mary Jo began to rediscover the beauty in life, she developed a renewed enthusiasm for activities that she had lost interest in, like traveling and knitting. She also signed up to substitute teaching and began holding retreats for introspective writing. Mary Jo still doesn't know who sent Dr. Liberman's book to her, but she continues to do color homeopathy daily, because it makes her feel good—mentally, emotionally and physically. "It's like my brain was rewired through the light and colors," she says. "I'm truly living again; I'm no longer just existing. I'll always miss my husband, but color homeopathy helped me find my way back to joy."

When asked in a subsequent interview to comment on both Mary Jo's story and on color therapy as a healing modality, Dr. Liberman said:

The idea of light as an integral part of life and creation was evident since the beginning of time. In fact, all life on earth evolved under the influence of light. That's why the portion of the Universe we reside in is called the Solar System, which means of or derived from light. Today, we know that all biological life is composed of and dependent upon light. All physiological functions are light-dependent.

Rainbows allow us to see the different colors of the light spectrum. Eastern mystics felt that each color of the rainbow corresponded energetically to a different energy center, or chakra, in the body. Many people use color for physical healing. However, I discovered that color was inseparably linked to our emotions. Each person seemed comfortable with some colors and uncomfortable with others.

The colors we like are related to the life experiences we are comfortable with. The colors we dislike, correspond to life experiences we tend to recoil from. Exposing someone to small doses of the colors that make them uncomfortable, eventually neutralizes their reactions to those colors. By uncovering our unresolved emotional issues and desensitizing ourselves from those past traumas, we are able to reduce a great deal of stress, resulting in greater awareness, more energy and a profound sense of wellness.

Color is everywhere around us. But it's only in the last century or so that modern science has begun seriously to investigate and confirm what the ancients knew about the profound effects it has on us physically and emotionally.

Chromotherapy

Throughout the ages, scientists and scholars have studied the psychological effects and therapeutic aspects of color and light. The ancient Egyptians, Greeks, and Chinese utilized chromotherapy to treat ailments and restore health by placing people in rooms that had been painted different colors. The Egyptians are said to have copied nature by painting their floors the same green as the grass and their ceilings, the colors of the sky. They also hung crystals and gemstones in the window apertures of their "healing rooms" as prisms to capture and reflect different colors into the room and on to patients.

Papyrus sheets dating back to 1550 BC reference color "cures." The *Nei Ching*, an ancient Chinese book of internal medicine that dates back over 2000 years, records color diagnoses.[76] The famous Persian polymath, Ibn Sina (also known as Avicenna), who is regarded as one of the most signifi-cant physicians, astronomers, thinkers and writers of the Islamic Golden Age, wrote about color therapy in his famous medical encyclopedia, *The Canon of Medicine*.[77] Believing color to be linked with symptoms, Avicenna created a chart that outlined the relationships between color, temperature, and physical conditions of the body.

Little was recorded about color in the thousand or so years after Avicenna, until the 19th century, when interest seems to have picked up again.

During the American Civil War, General Augustus Pleasonton conducted his own experiments. His book *The Influence Of The Blue Ray Of The Sunlight And Of The Blue Color Of The Sky*, published in 1876, detailed how the color blue can improve the growth of crops and livestock and can help heal diseases in humans.

The German writer and statesman, Johann Wolfgang von Goethe, was the first person to systematically study the physiological effects of color. In 1810, he published his *Theories of Color*, which he considered to be his most important work. Goethe divided colors into two groups. One group consisted of red, orange, and yellow, the colors that he claimed cause happiness. The other group contained green, blue, indigo, and violet, which he believed cause sadness. However, that was Goethe's belief. Personally, I think that red, orange, and yellow colors have a more stimulating effect, that green is a neutral color, and blue and purple are more calming and relaxing. This makes me wonder whether what Goethe interpreted as sadness was, in fact, merely evidence of people becoming calmer and less animated.

In 1877, Niels Finsen discovered that solar ultra-violet light inhibits the growth of bacteria. He studied the use of light in the healing of wounds and used red to inhibit the formation of smallpox scars. In 1896 he founded the Light Institute in Copenhagen, which was dedicated to the photo treatment of tuberculosis. Today, it is called the "Finsen Institute."

In 1878, Dr. Edwin Babbitt published *Principles of Light and Color* in which he described various techniques of healing with color. And in 1932, two psychologists from California scientifically showed that, in humans, blue light has a calming effect, and red light has a stimulating effect.

In 1933, Dinshah Ghadiali, a scientist from India, published *The Spectro Chromemetry Encyclopedia,* which laid the foundation for most modern color therapy. Ghadiali claimed to have discovered why and how different colored rays have various therapeutic effects on organisms. He believed that colors represent chemical potencies in higher octaves of vibration and that specific colors can either stimulate or inhibit the work of each organ or system.

Ghadiali also thought it was important to know the action of different colors on different bodily systems and organs. This knowledge allows us to apply the correct colors to balance those organs or systems that have become abnormal in their function or condition.

The Austrian philosopher and social reformer, Rudolph Steiner, also conducted investigations into the therapeutic use of color. Steiner related color to shape, form, and sounds and suggested that the vibrational quality of specific colors is amplified by some forms. He believed that certain combinations of color and shape have either destructive or regenerative effects on living organisms.

Steiner's work with color was continued by the late Theo Gimbel, who established the Hygeia Studios and College of Color Therapy in Great Britain. Gimbel explored the claims of Max Luscher, a former professor of psychology at Basel University, who said that color preferences demonstrate states of mind and/or glandular imbalances, and therefore can be used as the basis for physical and psychological diagnosis.

How Color Therapy Works

Even though we don't see it, the light around us contains the full spectrum of colors. Each color has its own frequency and vibration. In some natural healing schools of thought, different colors are believed to relate to different parts of our body. It's also believed that our tissues and organs need the same energies as light. When disease or injury disturbs the vibration of an organ or area of our body, applying the associated color frequency can restore the body to health. Eastern medical practice teaches that we have meridians, which carry energy through the body and connect to each organ. This is the theory behind acupuncture, which attempts to remove blockages to the energy flow.

Color is thought to do the same thing. Each color's vibration is associated with different attributes and qualities. It also can influence our emotions and well-being by supplying the frequency we need to keep our mind and body in balance. Color does not heal; but rather enables the body to heal itself.

When asked for his take on how color homeopathy works, Jacob Liberman said, "Colored light slips beneath our conscious awareness, reaching beyond the cerebral cortex and into the primitive brainstem that controls our innate response to color. It penetrates our emotional and memory centers while triggering significant psychophysiological responses. In bringing unresolved issues to conscious awareness, color homeopathy unearths the emotional roots of our visual field constriction, ultimately freeing us from our past trauma."

While we could argue that psychotherapy can accomplish the same thing, Dr. Liberman says that based on his clinical experience of using color homeopathically, viewing colored light can often access deep issues much faster. "Psychology works at the speed of life. Color homeopathy works at the speed of light, and its effect cannot be blocked with emotional resistance. As soon as you observe a certain color, there is an association. It is a primal experience."

As research and technological advancements provide more evidence for how shape, form, light, and color impact our physical, psychological, and emotional balance and health, color therapy is growing in acceptance and popularity. For example, neurologists have found that children with autism may be helped by the use of color. Blue color filters are helping dyslexics to read. And precision-tinted lenses were found in research conducted by Jie Huang of Michigan State University's Department of Radiology, to normalize brain activity in patients with migraine headaches, thereby preventing attacks from recurring.[78]

There are many ways to use color therapy, from eating specific-colored foods to choosing colored clothing and wearing colored gemstones and jewelry. We can sit under lamps that emit different colored lights. We can point colored lights at specific parts of our bodies using instruments such as the Chromalive® Color Therapy Penlight Set which is claimed to have been used at the Soho House in Los Angeles at the Academy Awards.[79] And we can apply other methods of color therapy, such as using color therapy oils or color baths and painting our walls specific colors. We can also use systems such as Aura-Soma oils, which utilize color, plant, and crystal energies to calm our energetic system or enhance our moods, emotions, and vitality. And, as we have learned from Mary Jo Zimmer's story, one of the easiest and most popular ways to use color is to wear color therapy glasses. If you would like to investigate color therapy glasses, check out Colorglasses.com. This website not only shares a wealth of information and articles about the potential therapeutic benefits of color therapy and colored glasses but also sells colored glasses individually and in sets for therapeutic and emotional purposes at a more affordable price.[80] Meanwhile, here's a brief rundown on some ways that color therapy is being used today.

Phototherapy

Phototherapy has been used for several decades in conventional medical practice to treat certain diseases. For example, it's used to direct ultraviolet light to the affected area in the treatment of psoriasis and acne. Blue light is used to treat pain and hyperbilirubinemia (jaundice), a liver condition in premature babies. And Light therapy is proving to be at least as effective as antidepressant medications for treating seasonal affective disorder (SAD). This entails sitting close to a special "light box" for 30 minutes a day, usually as soon after waking up as possible. These boxes provide 10,000 lux ("lux is a measure of light intensity), which is about 100 times brighter than the average indoor lighting. A bright sunny day is 50,000 lux or more.

The Relationship Between Light and Melatonin

Melatonin is a hormone that regulates your body's diurnal rhythm (its sleep-wake cycle). It is primarily released by the pineal gland. As a supplement, it is often used for the short-term treatment of sleep deprivation, such as usually occurs with jet lag, shift work, or at times of intense emotional or psychological anxiety. Sleep experts have known about the relationship between melatonin and light exposure for a long time. Light exposure suppresses melatonin production. This is why it's hard to sleep in a room that isn't dark. It's also why it's better to use subdued lighting or a night light in the bathroom if your sleep is regularly interrupted by the need to use the toilet.

In his book *Lights Out: Sleep, Sugar and Survival*, T.S. Wiley[81] states that if we do not sleep in the dark, our body does not produce the hormones (like melatonin and serotonin) it needs for energy for the waking day. He cites an experiment in which LED light directed at the back of people's knees disrupted the production of these hormones during sleep, even though no other lights were being directed at any other part of the body, or were even shining in the room. Basically, any light sensed by the body can disrupt it in many ways.

If you suffer from drowsiness in the afternoon, but can't afford to lose the time, sleep experts say that stepping outside and exposing yourself to sunlight will keep you awake and alert. Conversely, if you find it hard to get to sleep at night, wearing red or magenta glasses in the evening is said to help increase melatonin production by as much as 70 percent. Since I've been using amber-colored glasses to block out blue light exposure when working on my computer in the evenings, I have noticed a big change in how quickly my body winds down when I go to bed. It takes me far less time to fall asleep. (The best glasses I have found on the market are from Swanwicksleep.com.)

It is not difficult to become physically or emotionally out of balance. In color therapy, colors are often associated with specific emotions and feelings. For example, we will often say that someone is "green with envy" when they're feeling jealous, or they're "feeling blue," when they are feeling down or disappointed. We talk about "seeing red" when describing an angry moment or being "in a black mood" when we're feeling negative. It is said that the organs and glands of our bodies vibrate at specific frequencies and that colors correspond to the areas of our body which have the same vibration.

When we are sick, our organs and glands may become out of balance and not function at their proper frequencies. Here again, restoring the proper frequency using color is thought to help restore balance in that area of the body.

Color, Light, and Geometry –
The Spectrahue Method™ of Light Therapy

Julianne Bien is the inventor of the Spectrahue Method of Light Therapy.[82] She owns Spectrahue Light & Sound Inc., a Toronto-based company, which distributes original Lumalight hand-held tools, educational materials, and live training. Bien is a recognized authority in the esoteric knowledge of color and sacred shapes for spiritual and self-awareness pursuits. Her journey began in 1996 when she was guided to explore the mysteries and understanding of light as a language.

After traveling far and wide to study this subject, Bien realized the need for a gentle and versatile hand-held color delivery system. In 1999, she developed the first Lumalight set, which is different from the various light instruments used in therapies such as Low-Level Laser therapy and LED light therapy. Unlike traditional tools, Lumalight utilizes unique clip-on color filters and geometric shapes to create specific effects with the emitted light. This system, she says, can be easily learned and used in acupuncture and acupressure clinics, as well as other holistic practices.

Says Bien:

> The building blocks in our lives are nature's patterns and are known as the Platonic shapes, or polyhedrons. The ancient Greek philosopher, Plato, believed these forms were the basic components of the universe. The Spectrahue Method uses these designs in its own unique way. I believe each patterning is its own creative force. There is much more to discover about them.
>
> For simplicity's sake, I have termed the remaining designs in the series: cosmic geometry. Each of these intrinsic shapes has a unique use separate from the Platonic polyhedrons. I believe each hold organized universal principles and has a consciousness of its own when broadcast with color into the field.

Bien claims that her Lumalight penlight acts "as a translator of inner awareness that has no boundaries. Simply combine a geometric design with a color filter and project it into the aura. The purpose is to address certain blocks that may have smudged the etheric template and impeded its natural flow (this is the first layer of the aura closest to you). By shining light on this holographic sphere, one goal is to feel whole again; another may be to support you on a spiritual quest or help your meditative practice of reflection. This so-called layer of energy hosts all experiences, emotions, and challenges that are calling to be resolved or dissolved on an energetic level. See it as an imprint of an index file or flash drive stored in a place that you have access to. Your higher self, alongside your intuitive knowing and wisdom, knows where it is and knows the timing to access it."

Lumalight geometry inserts include several examples of sacred geometry shapes, including the infinity symbol and the Fibonacci Spiral, platonic forms such as the icosahedron, octahedron, star tetrahedron, Metatron's Cube and dodecahedron, cosmic shapes such as the pyramid, 4-point, 5-point-7-point and 9-point stars, and the Flower of Life, to name just a few.

According to Bien, the universal power of light energy, or color harmonics, as she calls her holistic application of color energy, is the giver of all life. Harnessing this power opens us up to almost limitless opportunities to improve our spiritual, emotional, and physical existence. "In essence," she says, "we are beings of light and need to keep our energy flowing freely for vitality and a positive outlook on life. We can nurture and support this natural process with the use of color. The use of color as a natural property of sunlight has entered the mainstream of alternative thinking, just as the Chinese art of acupuncture did many decades ago. Like acupuncture, color light applications are based on universal principles and point locations on the meridians used since ancient times."

Bien believes that color—both the visible and invisible kind—is a silent language we all know by heart deep inside us. Her 2004 book, *Golden Light: A Journey with Advanced Colorworks*, which provides information on the mystical side and meaning of color, has now been expanded into a five-part training series.

Other types of Color Therapy

Other types of Color Therapy that are proving popular today include:

Crystal Healing
This entails the laying on of stones to restore balance to the chakra system and heal the physical body, emotions, mental thoughts, and the spirit. Stones are placed based on color, quality, and sacred geometry formations.

Color Silks Therapy
This entails colored silks being placed over the chakra centers of the body.

Natural fabrics such as cotton and wool are also thought to carry healing vibrations. But silk is considered to have the highest frequency vibration and therefore is valued the most. We have found that synthetic fibers such as polyester and rayon block the free flow of energy, so we do not use them as blankets in the Egg. Instead, we use natural fiber blankets.

Colorpuncture and Samassati Color Therapy

Both of these use colored lights on meridians, acupoints, reflex zones, chakras, and the aura. Just as needling is used in acupuncture, and pressure is applied in acupressure and Shiatsu to meridians and acupoints, color in the form of light, crystals and essential oils is used to affect the electromagnetic circuity of the human system.[83]

Although Samassati Color Therapy has its roots in Colorpuncture, less emphasis is placed on following the techniques by rote, and more on sensing the effects of specific colors, using one's intuition to determine the appropriate colors and placements, and feeling the effects of color with all the various energy pathways of the client.[84]

As Julienne Bien claims, "Color is the language of light. It may also hold the secrets to accessing universal knowledge that exists within all of us. We just have to recognize it, then unlock the doors—with light."

The Hidden Magic and Meanings of Numbers

*"If you want to find the secrets of the universe,
think in terms of energy, frequency and vibration."*
— NIKOLA TESLA

Nikola Tesla[85] was a Serbian-American inventor, futurist, and electrical and mechanical engineer. Best known for his contributions to the design of the modern alternating current (AC) electricity supply system, Tesla is widely regarded as one of the greatest inventors of all time. Tesla once said: "If you only knew the magnificence of the 3, 6 and 9, then you would have the key to the universe," thereby leaving millions of people forever wondering, *what is so magnificent (or important) about the numbers three, six, and nine?*

To shed some light on this, we first need to go back to ancient Greece, and in particular, to the life and work of the Ionian Greek philosopher, Pythagoras of Samos, who lived from c.570-c.495 BC.[86] While knowledge of Pythagoras's life is said to be clouded by legend, he has been credited with many mathematical and scientific discoveries. These include Pythagorean theorem, the five regular (Platonic) solids, the Theory of Proportions, and identifying the morning and evening stars as the planet Venus. However, according to Wikipedia, the teaching most securely identified with Pythagoras, is known as metempsychosis, or the "transmigration of souls," which holds that every soul is immortal and upon death enters into a new body. The most important thing about Pythagoras (at least as far as this book is concerned), is that he is known as the father of Western Numerology.

Numerology is any belief in the divine or mystical relationship between a number and one or more coinciding events. It's also the study of the numerical value of the letters in words, names, and ideas. Pythagoras is said to have begun his theory of numbers by discovering the mathematical relationship between numbers and musical notes. He found that vibrations in stringed instruments could be mathematically explained. Pythagorean numerology uses an individual's name and date of birth. The name number reveals the individual's outer nature or the personality they present to the outside world. To start, you need to use the individual's full name as written on their birth certificate. Then, each letter is assigned to a number one to nine, based on the ancient Pythagorean system.

The Greek philosopher, Aristotle, claimed that the Pythagoreans used mathematics for solely mystical reasons because they believed that all things were made of numbers. The number one represented the origin of all things (the monad, the supreme being or divinity), and the number two (the dyad, the principle of "twoness" or "otherness") represented matter. The number three was considered an "ideal number" because it had a beginning, middle, and end and was the smallest number of points that could be used to define a plane triangle, which they revered as a symbol of the god Apollo.

The Number "Three"—Key to the Hidden Mysteries of the Universe?

Throughout human history, the number three has always had a unique significance. It appears in religion, architecture, and mathematics, and many cultures believed that this number represents something sacred, mystical, universal, and divine. In mythology, the destiny of gods and man is said to be controlled by all-powerful beings known as the Three Fates.

For Pythagoras, and for a lot of ancient philosophers, mathematics was the way something supernatural could be explained. Many scientists and inventors, including Nikola Tesla, ascribed extreme importance to the number three. Pythagoras taught that everything in the Universe has a three-part structure. He also stated that every problem in the world could be reduced diagrammatically to a triangle and the number three. To Pythagoras and his followers, the triangle represented ascension, and the triangle and number three is the key to all hidden mysteries in the universe. However, Pythagoras was not the first to discover the importance of the number three. He received the knowledge from the Egyptians, who claimed that their information came directly from the "Gods." He was the first to both spread this knowledge outside of Egypt and to speak about a sacred or divine knowledge that came from the "Gods." Many believe that the Pythagorean triangle may contain wisdom that we still haven't understood in terms of how physical-terrestrial geometry can connect to otherworldly domains that possibly coexist with our own.

The Number "Three" and the DNA Code

All living organisms are dependent on three types of large molecules for all of their biological functions. These molecules are DNA, RNA, and proteins. DNA makes RNA, which then makes proteins. Without these three molecules, life in any form could not exist.

In 1966, scientists announced they had successfully deciphered the Genetic Code with the discovery that the structure of our DNA consists of a series of three molecule combinations known as triplets. The genetic code consists of three-letter "words" called codons, which are formed from a sequence of three nucleotides (e.g., ACT, CAG, TTT). This makes the number three very important as you can say that it represents the key to our existence, the key to understanding the complex DNA language.

Isaac Newton and the Alchemy of "Three"

One of the most influential scientists of the 17th century was Isaac Newton. Newton introduced what became the basis of all modern physics: the three laws of motion. But what many people don't know is that Isaac Newton was a mystic who was extremely interested in alchemy. A translation of an ancient document called "the Emerald Tablet" was said to have been found among his philosophy, astronomy, and mathematics documents. The "Emerald Tablet" is also known as the *Smaragdine Table*, or *Tabula Smaragdina*. It has fascinated alchemists for hundreds of years because it was thought to be one of several tablets that contained esoteric information on the practice of alchemy and the entire knowledge of the

Universe, including the ancient wisdom of transmutation, and the secrets of the cosmos and longevity. According to researchers, these tablets were discovered in the Great Pyramids thousands of years ago.

3-6-9 The Tesla Code, or The Mathematical Fingerprint of God

Vortex Based Mathematics (VBM) is a revolutionary system involving whole numbers, toroidal constructs, and spirituality that explains the science of our Interdimensional Universe. It was discovered by Marko Rodin and is said to provide humanity with a unique and important key to the new interdimensional science we are seeking.[87] This is how one website describes Rodin's discovery of Vortex Mathematics:

> Marko studied all the world's great religions. He decided to take "The Most Great Name of Bahaullah" (prophet of the Bahai Faith) which is Abha and convert it into numbers. He did this in an effort to discover the true precise mystical intonation of "The Most Great Name of God." Since the Bahai sacred scripture was originally written in Persian and Arabic, Marko used the Abjad numerical notation system for this letter to number translation.
>
> This was a sacred system of allocating a unique numerical value to each letter of the 27 letters of the alphabet so that secret quantum mechanic physics could be encoded into words. What Marko discovered was that (A=1, b=2, h=5, a=1) = 9. The fact that The Most Great Name of God equaled 9 seemed very important to him as everything he had read in both the Bahai scriptures and other religious text spoke of nine being the omni-potent number. So next he drew out a circle with nine on top and 1 through 8 going around the circle clockwise. Then he discovered a very intriguing number system within this circle. Marko knew he had stumbled upon something very profound. This circle with its hidden number sequence was the "Symbol of Enlightenment." This is the *Mathematical Fingerprint Of God*.

In Vortex Math, if you polarize everything, the numbers 1,2,4,5,7,8 are numbers that represent the physical world, and the numbers 3,6,9 are numbers that represent the spiritual world, which governs the physical world from the quantum level. In Vortex Math, number 9 is the most recurring number when adding up the sides or the circumference of a circle, and other shapes. Here are some examples: The circumference of a circle is 360 degrees, which is 3+6+0=9. The diameter of a circle is 180 degrees, which is 1+8+0=9. The radius of a circle is 90 degrees, which is 9+0=9. If you add up all the angles of a triangle you get 90+90+90=270, which is 2+7+0=9.

The angles of a square are 90+90+90+90=360, which is 3+6+0=9. In a 3D square you have 8 angles which add up to 90x8=720, which is 7+2+0=9. In a pyramid you have five angles, which add up to 90x5=450, which is 4+5+0=9, and so on. Each shape also corresponds to notes on the harmonic scale tuned to 432 Hz (4+3+2=9) all add up to numbers 3,6,9.

Many researchers believe that it is through this discovery, which has become known as The Tesla Code, that Tesla discovered that the universe is made out of energy, vibration, and frequency. According to the Tesla Code, thought, feelings, and beliefs combine to make up vibrational frequencies which reshape the universe around us from the quantum level all the way up to the physical world. In other words, thoughts, feelings, and beliefs are spiritual non-physical things that affect the physical universe around us because we are energetically and vibrationally one with it. Many people believe that the Tesla Code is the missing link to the law of attraction taught in the movie *The Secret*.

If you search the internet, using the phrases the Tesla Code, Numerology, and the 3-6-9 phenomenon, you will find innumerable references to articles, reports, and documents which make the case for, and also argue against, the veracity of the information that abounds about the Tesla Code.

Sacred Geometry and the Harmonic Egg

The fact that the Harmonic Egg is designed with this in mind will tell you that I agree with him. Not just because I've researched the alchemy of these numbers for myself. But because long before I knew about sacred geometry and numerology, I was "told" (or received what I consider to be divinely inspired information) that these numbers had a vital role to play in the manufacture of the Harmonic Egg.

- The Harmonic Egg is a dodecahedron (i.e., 12-sided 2-dimensional) structure on the outside. In numerology, the number 12 reduces to a 3—(1+2=3).

- The Harmonic Egg contains a hexagon-shaped (i.e., six-sided) platform on the inside, where the zero-gravity chair sits.

- The interior of the Egg is a full 360-degree circle, which, in numerology is a 9—(3+6=9).

Furthermore, the music that is played in the Egg has been carefully composed, selected, and studied to work within the geometric pattern inside.

When I select music for the Harmonic Egg, I consider many vital factors. One is the consciousness of the composer/musicians. Another is how the music has been mastered and recorded. A third is how it feels to my body inside the Harmonic Egg. There is wonderful music available that just does not work within the Harmonic Egg. It's not bad. There is nothing wrong with it. It's merely that I believe the Egg is a high vibrational apparatus. Hence, the music played inside it must match that vibration to resonate and work with the individuals who use it. Some musicians have the intention for healing, and there are others whose intention is focused on making money. There is a vibrational consciousness in both energies. Some pieces of music are not mastered or recorded well, and they are "flat" in the Egg. I hear and feel the music in the Egg differently than anyone, but I believe I have been given the gift of "hearing" what the Eggs wish to project for the clients that enter them.

CHAPTER ELEVEN

The Magic of Intention, Manifestation, and Having a Good Vibration

"Everything that happens in the universe begins with intention.
Intention is the starting point of every dream.
It is the creative power that fulfills all of our needs,
whether for money, relationships, spiritual awakening, or love."
—DEEPAK CHOPRA

In an article titled *5 Steps to Harness the Power of Intention*, which began with the quote above, Deepak Chopra shared:

The sages of India observed thousands of years ago that our destiny is ultimately shaped by our deepest intentions and desires. The classic Vedic text, the Upanishads declare: 'You are what your deepest desire is. As your desire is, so is your intention. As your intention is, so is your will. As your will is, so is your deed. As your deed is, so is your destiny.' [88]

From the day I decided to leave the corporate world behind to pursue my dream of making a difference by opening a wellness center, every decision I have made, and everything I have engaged in, has been conceived and undertaken with a very clear intention. Over the years, I have written more than a few articles on intention and manifestation. When clients come for Harmonic Egg sessions, I hold as sacred the rule that, when conducting client intakes, the attending practitioner or technician encourages the client to set an intention for their session. Whether they want to attract a new career, have perfect health, restore their quality of life, improve a relationship, or get a new puppy, I encourage clients to imagine what it would feel like in ALL the cells of their being to already have that intention be true. I tell them they do not have to focus on it the entire time, but just spend a few minutes *really* feeling it and embodying it before they settle back to either fall asleep or merely enjoy their relaxation time in the Harmonic Egg.

One of the reasons I do this is because my belief in the power of intention is unquestionable. Another reason is that I have learned that the Harmonic Egg can amplify one's intentions. Indeed, some clients have even started referring to the Egg as their "manifestation Egg."

Of course, one doesn't have to have access to a Harmonic Egg to start cultivating the practice of setting one's intention. I just find that the sacred geometry, sound, and lights in the Egg, amplify intentions. Setting your intention can also be a great practice to cultivate before starting your day.

How Do We Know Intention Works?

In Chapter Seven, "Believe it And You'll See It," we explored the Placebo Effect, its implications on the power of intention, and how the research of scientists and doctors such as Bruce Lipton, Larry Dossey, and Candace Pert demonstrates that the mind can provoke physical changes inside of us. We also learned from the work of Masuru Emoto and Dean Radin that the mind is capable of affecting the world *outside* of us. Rupert Sheldrake is another scientist whose work has demonstrated that our thoughts, and therefore our intentions, can have repercussions outside of ourselves.

Intention, Quantum Entanglement, and Dogs Who Know When Their Owners Are Coming Home

Rupert Sheldrake is a biologist and author best known for his hypothesis of morphic resonance. This is the idea that natural systems have a collective memory and that beings in these systems are connected through a morphic field. This phenomenon is explained by the theory of quantum entanglement, which is based on the idea that if consciousness does not reside in the brain, then the minds of beings that are closely connected can become entangled. To test this, Rupert Sheldrake conducted several research studies on dogs and their owners.

The results were published in his book *Dogs that Know When Their Owners are Coming Home*. They were also recorded in a documentary program broadcast on British television, which showed that dogs could sense, even at large distances, when their human companions had made the decision to return home. The results were statistically significant, with almost 60% of dogs filmed going to the door as soon as their owner had the intention to come back and remaining there until their arrival. Sheldrake's explanation is that mental intention can be communicated via morphogenetic fields.

My boyfriend tells me that whenever I text him to say that I am leaving the office and on my way to his place, his dog immediately goes to the window and waits for me to arrive. I also find it fascinating when I arrive at the barn and get out of my car, I often hear my horse "talking" to me. Yet she cannot even see me from the parking lot. Nonetheless, it makes my day when she acknowledges my arrival.

Many massage therapists and practitioners who work closely with clients have reported knowing their intention while giving a massage or treatment profoundly affects their clients' experiences. My experience with clients supports this. Hence, my strict rule that all the staff I train are cognizant of this and make every effort to maintain a positive mood and outlook when working directly with clients.

The Autism Intention Experiments

Dr. William A. Tiller has spent 40-plus years researching consciousness. A pioneer of psychoenergetics since the 1960s, Dr. Tiller was a professor of Materials Science at Stanford University for 30 years and also worked in private industry. Dr. Tiller pioneered the original intention experiments when he created a rigorous experimental protocol for proving that our intentions can create meaningful alterations in the space around us, as well as within us.

Dr. Tiller is the author of several ground-breaking books on psychoenergetic science, including *Science and Human Transformation: Subtle Energies, Intentionality and Consciousness*, *Conscious Acts of Creation: The Emergence of a New Physics*, and *Some Science Adventures with Real Magic*, as well as more than 150 published papers concerning unactualized human capabilities, opportunities, and adventures. Dr. Tiller's experiments clearly demonstrate that human intention can indeed change materials and living systems in a beneficial way when he proved that focused intention has the power to transform the pH balance of water thousands of miles away. [89]

Dr. Tiller became known to millions around the world when he appeared as a featured physicist in the ground-breaking movie, *What the Bleep Do We Know?* When I first saw the film it resonated deeply with me. It was my first introduction to Dr. Joe Dispenza, with whom I once spent a few hours in Boulder, Colorado, chatting about our work with sound and light modalities. If you've ever wanted to understand psychoenergetic phenomena such as remote viewing, psychokinesis, auras, clairvoyance and clairaudience, precognition, levitation, materialization/dematerialization, telepathy and healing, Dr. Tiller has provided qualitative explanations based on real, solid science.

Suzy Miller is a former Pediatric Speech-Language Pathologist with a Master's Degree in Education. Her paradigm-shifting exchanges with a non-verbal child diagnosed with autism in 1999 triggered a series of profound understandings, which led to the birth of a unique body of work that has pioneered a shift in the perception of autism from an individual "disorder" to a collective revolution in human consciousness.[90]

A visionary speaker, author, telepathic communicator, and multidimensional seer, Miller is the founder of the groundbreaking Awesomism Practitioner Process, which now has over 150 practitioners around the world, as well as the author of the book *Awesomism: A New Way to Understand the Diagnosis of Autism*. Miller's work with autistic children and adults has profoundly shifted the perception of what many regarded as a devastating disorder from Autism to Awesomism. In taking something synonymous with the word "broken" and shining a light on its hidden potential, she not only transformed the lives and the outlook for thousands of parents and children worldwide, but also gave birth to a powerful new word that is rich with positive potential.

Throughout her long career, Suzy Miller has collaborated with professionals in a variety of fields, from psychology, social work, mainstream education, and medicine to leading-edge scientists, metaphysicians, healers, and new thought leaders. Having heard, from the collective consciousness of the children, specific details regarding the requirements necessary for autistics to fully integrate into the physical experience, it was inevitable that when Suzy met Dr. Tiller, he should hypothesize whether it was possible "to support the integration of children diagnosed with autism through the utilization of a consistent and coherent intention."

In December 2012, Dr. Tiller and Suzy Miller spearheaded an experiment that they believed could forever change the way the world perceives and approaches the condition of autism. Astonishingly, even before the official start of the intention experiment, parents around the world were contacting Miller with reports of positive reactions and changes they were witnessing in their children. And within one day of the official commencement, a previously non-verbal child in Australia spoke and displayed other positive behavioral changes.

While the experiment was conducted specifically with energetically sensitive children and those diagnosed on the spectrum, both Dr. Tiller and Suzy Miller agree that the implications of their findings "extended far beyond this population to encompass every single human on the planet." They believe their findings prove that we are all multidimensional beings with gifts and capabilities far beyond what many currently believe. Moreover, each one of us can use the power of intention to direct and transform our own lives in any way we wish.

When I met Suzy, it was a day like any other day, when I suddenly got an urgent FaceTime call from Sandie, who was with Suzy at the time. At first, I wondered why they were calling, and who on earth was Suzy Miller? But by the end of our short call, I was crying. And so was Suzy Miller, who had shared with me some startling insights about the Harmonic Egg, and its possibilities. Three days later, Suzy was standing in front of me, having made a snap decision to fly from Los Angeles to Denver to experience the Egg for herself. She had to know whether the Egg was the 'Pod' that the Collective Consciousness of the Children had been telling her was soon going to appear in the physical.

Suzy's report of her experience, and her evaluation of the role the Egg has to play in helping those diagnosed with autism to integrate more fully in their bodies is shared in Part III. When she invited me to join her for an interview about the Harmonic Egg, which she was organizing for her followers and certified practitioners, I was delighted. From the moment of our first meeting, when we both wept, I've felt as though Suzy and I are "sisters from another mother."

Using Your Thoughts to Change Your Life and Your World

In 2008, bestselling author of *The Field*, Lynne McTaggart, published *The Intention Experiment: Using Your Thoughts to Change Your Life and the World*. In it, she shared exciting developments in the science of intention. She also profiled several scientists and renowned pioneers who had been studying the effects of focused group intention on scientifically quantifiable targets such as animals, plants, and humans.[91]

McTaggart's book offers a practical program designed to help readers get in touch with their own thoughts, to increase the activity and strength of their intentions, and to begin achieving real change in their lives. She then invited them to participate in an unprecedented experiment by becoming part of scientific history. They had to focus their power of intention on specific targets, and using The Intention Experiment website, coordinate their involvement and track results of their own and other participants around the world.

While I enjoyed *The Field*, my life is so busy, I need more accessible tools to manifest in my life. Fortunately, I have found ways to make it easier, one of which involves the Harmonic Egg. I remember taking a class on intention with my sister, Gloria, in which the instructor spoke about the importance of clearing negative energies from objects, and blessing your food before eating, etc. However, her list of things that need to be done to clear energy was so long that Gloria took one look at it, and declared, "I don't have time for all that. I have a six-year-old child." After some pondering, I got an intuitive hit that all one really need do is hold or touch the object and say, "Clear. Clear. Clear," and it will be done. People do like to complicate things. But setting your intention doesn't have to be difficult. It's not a complicated or long-winded process. It just has to be your intention!

Another well-known teacher that inspired me was Wayne Dyer. He was the first teacher I studied. When I started my spiritual journey in 1998, I couldn't get enough of his information. I played his cassette tapes over and over again whenever I was driving my car. His book, *The Power Of Intention: Learning to Co-create Your World Your Way* explored intention not as something we do, but as an invisible field of energy that we are all a part of and can access to begin co-creating our life. Dyer said, "When we train ourselves to tune into it and step beyond our minds and egos, we become, 'connectors' and make ourselves available to the energy of success." He described connectors as "the people whom everyone sees as lucky, the people who get all the breaks. They don't say, 'With my luck, everything will go wrong.' They just know things will go well. They trust an invisible force that will be all-providing, and just don't attract negativity to themselves."

After reading his book, which is full of ideas and steps that can help you tap into this transformational energy, I set my intention to meet him. And I did. When I managed to get tickets to one of his events for me and my then-boyfriend, David Stanley, I was as giddy as a schoolgirl. Though David was less than excited. As soon as Wayne had finished his talk, I pushed my way up to the stage. I wanted a photo of us together and was thrilled when he said yes. He was so sweet and had a kind and caring energy. The photo was very intimate as he squeezed me really tight to him. I couldn't wait to show the photograph to my parents. My dad took one look at the way

Wayne was holding me and immediately exclaimed, "Who is that guy?" I said, "Dad, that's Wayne Dyer!" My dad merely stated that he didn't like how close he was holding me. I chuckled at his response.

I have always been good at manifesting, although I didn't fully appreciate that until later in life. I used to think that everyone could pick up a book and open it to a page with precisely the answer they were seeking. For me, it's always about being in the flow. We've all had times in our lives when everything is flowing along quite smoothly. Then suddenly, we hit a brick wall, and everything stops flowing. What causes that? In my experience, getting out of the flow is like changing the radio frequency from a station that plays happy, uplifting music to one playing music that just makes you cringe. We all know what that's like. You're grooving along, listening to your favorite radio station—perhaps classic rock—enjoying all the great memories associated with the songs that are playing. Then, all of a sudden, someone switches the dial to a station playing heavy metal or rap, or music that you dislike. Within seconds, your nerves are jangling, and your mood abruptly shifts as the mellow feelings you were enjoying rapidly evaporate. Now you're feeling out of sorts, irritated, and annoyed by the intrusion. And, somehow, you've got to find your way back to your comfortable, happy station.

I spent several years of my life attracting alcoholics, narcissists, and sociopathic men. It was my normal. I was jogging along, tuned in to a radio station that really wasn't the right frequency for me. But I didn't know what I didn't know. Once I started using sound and light modalities, however, my vibration subtly started to change. Before long, I wasn't resonating with that same frequency. My radio station had changed, and I stopped attracting the kinds of men that operated on that vibrational frequency. It was an eye-opening experience.

From that moment on, I set my intention on finding a man that was on the right frequency for me. Someone who would treasure me and care for me as I would cherish and care for him. I made a list of the qualities I wanted this man to have and the kind of relationship that we would have together, and I pinned it on my fridge. Five years ago, I met Bill. A Harley dude, a retired US Navy chief petty officer, and an all-round amazing man, Bill is my Viking warrior. Without a doubt, the best man I have attracted into my life. Raised by a Mexican mom and a Texan father, Bill was taught to respect a lady and to hold a space for her to be a divine feminine goddess. I cannot say enough about how much he helps me. He travels with me for business. He is my travel agent, my driver, my healthy food and fresh juice scout when we're on the road. He is observant of my needs on every level. Ladies, if you don't have your Bill yet, he's out there. All you have to do is set a strong, clear intention, and hold to it.

Remember, as Deepak Chopra says: *"Everything that happens in the universe begins with intention. Intention is the starting point of every dream. Just keep in mind to be careful what you wish for, be specific and remember that thoughts become things."*

Part II of this book has provided a very brief overview of the frequencies of energy, sound, light, color, and how these frequencies are now being investigated, researched, and tested in various areas. These include the mainstream medical field as well as the therapeutic, and perhaps even some fringe areas of alternative and complementary medicine. I included this information to give you some background information and research to understand why and how the Harmonic Egg could accomplish the extraordinary things you are going to read about in Part III.

Before you turn to this next section, however, I want to remind you that while I am happy to take credit for the development, organization, and manufacture of the Harmonic Egg, I do not claim to be its "creator." Instead, I firmly believe that its existence is evidence of a remarkable act of co-creative energy input between me and an unseen source of higher consciousness.

IMPORTANT NOTE

Please note that while I have covered a number of different healing modalities in this part of the book, I am acutely aware that, like all of us, practitioners and therapists are not immune from emotional and psychological ups and downs. Thus, it is essential when seeking healing from another person to be extremely discerning in your choice of practitioner, as well as the overall energies of any healers that you spend time with or from whom you receive healing assistance.

PART III

Harmonic Egg Experiences

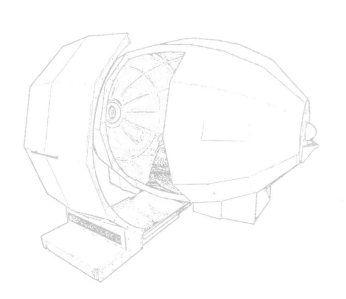

Yuval's Story

*"A World Class Composer and Musician's Experience
with Sound in the Harmonic Egg."*

YUVAL RON is a world-renowned musician, composer, educator, peace activist, and record producer with numerous awards to his name, and many successful collaborations with master musicians, artists, and well-known choreographers. Noted for his musical genius, and for composing the music for the Oscar-winning film *West Bank Story*, Yuval was invited to perform for the Dalai Lama and has collaborated with Sufi leaders, Zen Buddhist priests, visual artists, internationally known choreographers and neuro-scientists such as Andrew Newbury and Mark Robert Waltman. A noted lecturer, Yuval has spoken at Yale, John Hopkins, UCLA, MIT, and other schools, and has been on the faculty of Esalen Institute. His book *Divine Attunement: Music as a Path to Wisdom*, earned him the Gold Medal at the Indie Book Awards in 2015 for Best Book in the Spirituality Category.

As mentioned in Part II, I met Yuval after contacting his company Metta Mindfulness Music, which he co-founded with Dr. Richard Gold. I wanted to discuss the possibility of creating private label music exclusively for use in the Harmonic Egg. As luck—or synchronicity—would have it, Yuval was scheduled shortly to embark on a ten-day concert tour in Colorado. I invited him to stop by to discuss music and experience the Harmonic Egg for himself.

After his first session in the Harmonic Egg, during which he experienced his own music, Yuval had a lot to say—both as an individual receiving a Harmonic Egg session and also as a master musician and composer evaluating the music and sound inside the Egg. I was astonished when Yuval described his personal experience in the Egg as akin to achieving "shavasana" within just 20 minutes of entering the Egg. If you're not familiar with yoga, "shavasana," which is also known as the "corpse" position, is the final relaxation and integration part of a yoga session. It's the part that everyone looks forward to the most in any session. Here's what Yuval had to say about it:

> "... the whole point of the yoga is to get to that last ten or five minutes when you lay down and you really surrender and let go. It could be the

deepest experience of the whole yoga session, but it takes an hour and a half to get people to stretch and create space, and meditate to finally let go of all the muscles and be open to something that they may receive in shavasana... I experienced that in the Egg about 20 minutes into it. My hands just slipped off the armrest. I felt my eyelids slowly become heavier, and I thought *I'm getting so relaxed that I'm going to fall asleep.*"

Yuval was also surprised that he felt such a deep emotional response to the music, which was, he said, "deeper than listening to the music in a regular listening experience." He was also captivated by the increased appeal of listening to his own music in the Egg environment, and witnessing what he described as "an enhanced beauty that I had never heard in that music I'm so familiar with."

"Gail played me my own composition, which is the six healing sounds, and when I heard the first track which is metal... then water and then wood ... a 30-minute experience, I felt tears in my throat. I never heard my own music in such a way; it was really gorgeous, and it felt like waves were just continually arising. You know, the music was not just floating but it was, separate, the different elements in the music became, very clearly like waves of sound washing over you again, and again, and again.

I learned a lot from it in order to compose the custom-made music for that space. So, I heard elements that I created, which were spectacular, and other elements that were just okay, which sounded like they did in any other environment. So that was a very interesting experience."

Yuval compared the movement of sound within the Egg to the sound in cathedrals, saying "in some cathedrals, music would sound cold, or it would sound too boom-y, or not as beautiful." And in another cathedral, "the sound would be rich and perfectly balanced, and it has to do with architecture." He believes the architecture of the Egg itself gives it the ability to move sound in the way it does so that the person in the Egg experiences the music as if in surround-sound. He concluded that the positioning of the speakers inside the Egg not only gives one the feeling of being inside headphones but also fills the body with the vibrations of the sounds:

"So, the left speaker is facing your left ear, the right speaker is facing your right ear, and it's almost like you are inside headphones. It's like the setting of the headphones, but it's not on your ear. It's...I don't know, maybe six or eight feet away from you, pointing to your ear. That's where the speakers are, on the far left and the far right. And then the sound travels through the Egg, behind you, above you, in front of you, below you, and creates wonderful, wonderful sound reflections, which are sound waves that are traveling from every surface in the Egg towards your ears. So, the listening experience is much more complex."

Sharing his thoughts about how the Harmonic Egg works, and who would most benefit from sessions, Yuval believed the deep relaxation experienced in the Harmonic Egg would benefit people with "muscle tension, or inflammation … back pain, hamstring tightness, etc." He also felt that children with ADHD, or "hyper energy issues" would benefit from Egg sessions due to the deep relaxation it induces without requiring drugs, "just sound and sacred geometry." He concluded that the sacred geometry and measurements of the Harmonic Egg create its unique healing environment:

"I'm guessing that the sacred geometry and the golden ratio measurements that Gail used create the most harmonious, multi-reflective surfaces within the Egg. And so, although we are sending only two tracks left and right into that space, the amount of reflections from different areas around you throw the sound back at you in many different reflections.

… And the proof of the pudding is in the eating. And I can tell you that I experienced it with music I composed, which I know inside and out, and which I've heard on many different speakers and [in] many different spaces, and my own music in that space sounded just terrific. It brought me to tears, it was so beautiful."

Karen's Story

"Multidimensional Epiphanies, and Elevated States of Meditation and Spirituality."

KAREN BASKALL is a forty-nine-year-old elite athlete, a professional fitness model, and a national level bodybuilder and figure competitor. She has worked in the health and fitness industry for thirty years.

I came to meet Karen through mutual friends who were clients of the Metabolic Research Center in Westminster, Colorado, where Karen works, and where I was invited to speak. In discussing various aspects of assisting clients with health issues, Karen and I developed a professional relationship as well as a friendship.

When Karen came for a session at my Center, it was initially out of curiosity; she wanted to see what the Egg would feel like. Once she experienced it, however, she felt it would help prepare her body, mind, and spirit for an upcoming major surgical procedure. Karen's years as an elite athlete had left her with a shoulder injury that had become so painful, her only hope of finding relief lay in having her shoulder completely replaced. Karen knew that the procedure would be quite traumatic for her both physically and emotionally, and the projected recovery time was quite prolonged.

When she first experienced the Egg, Karen had found it to be so calming and relaxing that she had fallen asleep. That had surprised Karen as relaxing was something that she had been finding very hard to achieve. Somehow, said Karen, the Egg brought her to a place where she could shut the world down, and relax and sleep. According to Karen, she slept for about the first twenty minutes. She was then able to relax and take in the music and the meditative healing aspect for the second half of her session. During that time, she said she could feel her cells vibrating as she experienced an "increase in the vibrational level of the cells of my body, my soul, and my spirit." Further sessions proved to be a multidimensional experience for Karen, as she found herself more able to resolve problems and achieve a satisfactory closure to issues that she had been working on. Says Karen:

"I don't want to call them epiphanies, but things that I'd been thinking about or working came to conclusion... Multidimensional would be a good way to describe it, because you're feeling your body... physically feeling what it's doing, and you're hearing the music, but it is taking you to an elevated state, to a level of meditation and spirituality where you feel in tune. It's a beautiful feeling."

Karen scheduled several Harmonic Egg sessions both before and post-surgery. She was surprised to find that her healing and recovery progressed at an astonishingly rapid rate.

"I've been going every other week now... I'm only one month out, and I don't even see the surgeon until six weeks, and I can move my shoulder much more easily than I would have expected at this point. The physical therapists that I meet with twice a week are in utter disbelief."

Karen reports that in addition to sleeping better at night, the Harmonic Egg has brought her to a place of increased rest and higher meditation.

"I am walking, living proof, and people see that, and I do believe that I would not have healed as quickly without it. Having experienced the Harmonic Egg before the surgery, I knew it was something I wanted in place to get through it. So, whether or not we'd ever be able to prove it doesn't really matter, because I am living proof."

Michael's Story

An Internationally-renowned Cellist and Composer's "Return to Innocence."

MICHAEL FITZPATRICK is an American cellist and composer. The recipient of The Prince Charles Award for Musical Excellence conferred by His Royal Highness The Prince of Wales, Michael is the founder, chairman and artistic director of Millenia Music and its Earth's Call production. Michael has performed in concerts across the USA, Canada and Europe, the former Soviet Union, the Middle East, India, and Australia.

He's also performed as cello soloist at The Hollywood Bowl, Lincoln Center, Town Hall, and the Aspen Music Festival. On top of that, he has musically collaborated for the past twenty years with the Dalai Lama as part of Tuning The Planet, an East-West musical recording conducted inside the largest cave in the world, *Mammoth Cave National Park*.

Michael first came to the Life Center after being referred by a friend who was very enthusiastic about the value and vibrational healing potential of the light box, which was the precursor to the Harmonic Egg. Having found his experiences in the light box to be "quite radical," Michael was eager to experience what the Harmonic Egg could accomplish for him when it was completed.

> "From the very first session, people have said I look younger. I *feel* younger, and calmer, as well as more connected and energized... But it's a deep, calm energy state rather than an outer-world sort of frenetic adrenaline pump, hyper-energy state."

Having experienced numerous sessions in the Egg, Michael says that his experiences differ every time. He believes this is because the Harmonic Egg has a consciousness of its own and can also read the consciousness of anyone coming into it.

> "I think the Egg responds to whatever state I am in... similar to what happens when I sit down with my cello to play a concert, it basically reads the energy field and then plays that field, and anything that is out of tune

then gets tuned by it. The biggest thing for me is the nature of what I do, and the amount of traveling I do. I have a ridiculously high stress load, and I've been in all kinds of different body states, jetlag states, mental overload states related to production, etc.

Whenever I am in the Egg, I experience a deep, clarifying calm where anything discordant gets rendered out. There's something specific about what it is able to do... it's as if it is able to get inside the connecting meshing between the cells, or in the cells themselves, but sonically, it's able to penetrate spaces that most energetic healing modalities like Reiki cannot do because they're not using sound. And I think, from a musician's standpoint, the important distinction of why it works is in the sound. As our late great friend Don Campbell said, 'Sound is the medicine of the future.'"

After much thought, Michael concludes that the Egg helps people to ground their soul into their body. He also senses that, when in the Egg, one needs consciously to choose to engage with it in order to experience the full potential of the creative potential it offers.

"I see it as like some sort of innocence chamber, or birthing chamber; a place where we can go back to our source self, where we can calibrate back to that purity which gets battered by everything that's going on out there, and gives us the space to create everything anew - new ideas, new faculties, new neural pathways, new nervous system attenuation, and new heart capacities.

I'm not having a musical experience when I'm in it. I'm having what I have come to call a biofield experience. That's the way I just conceptually hold it. And I have no doubt that it is making me a better musician. Best of all, is that I always feel more connected to myself. I don't feel fragmented. And you can physically see the effects that it's had, so that's quite telling to me."

Kendra's Story

"A Miraculous Recovery From Chronic Fatigue and Illness!"

KENDRA SMITH was a project manager overseeing classroom libraries for a major publishing company. A diligent and committed manager, Kendra's working days regularly spanned ten to fifteen hours. But aware of the dangers of overwork, Kendra sensibly safeguarded her health by ensuring that she both exercised and ate well. But then a year of unforeseen painful life experiences propelled her over the stress threshold, severely compromising her immune system. First, she lost her grandmother. Then she lost her dog and a new puppy that she had rescued. Worst of all, her father, whom she regarded as her best friend, became seriously ill. Simultaneously, unexpected changes in her job required her to work longer and more arduous hours.

As her father lay slowly declining in the ICU, Kendra did her best to keep all the plates in her life spinning. Between juggling a heavy work schedule, visiting her father, and trying to maintain her home life with her husband, there was little room for taking good care of herself. Without fully realizing what was happening, Kendra's exercise and healthy eating regimes slowly began to suffer as the stress piled on. Despite being hospitalized with a severe bout of food poisoning, Kendra was determined to keep going. Determined to live as normal a life as possible, she continued seeing friends, attending church and supporting her father as his health continued to decline. Unaware that she was operating on fight or flight mode, and was slowly draining her body's physical and emotional reserves of energy, Kendra soldiered on. When she started experiencing anxiety after her father's death, she saw her doctor, who prescribed anti-depressant medication.

Five months after her Kendra's father's passing, she and her husband took a much-needed, short vacation to Mexico with a group of friends to attend a wedding. After the stress of the previous year, she reveled in her first break in months. She spent time having fun with her friends, snorkeling, dancing, sunbathing, and celebrating with a few drinks here and there.

Then, without warning, Kendra's body ran out of fuel. Overnight, her adrenal system crashed. She awoke the following morning, utterly exhausted and without energy even to move. Says Kendra:

"I blamed being extremely lethargic on having had two busy days and late nights in a row, and the few extra drinks I should not have had. But as the day continued and everyone else met at the pool to enjoy our last few days in Mexico, I just couldn't muster the energy to get out of bed. My husband worried and didn't want to leave me alone in our hotel, but I insisted I was okay and just needed some rest!

I awoke that evening to find myself lying in a pool of sweat and shaking with cold chills, and still feeling exhausted. Now I knew there was something wrong. I had slept for almost 24 hours, and had missed the dinner boat cruise with the bride and groom that we had scheduled a few days before. My husband had gone alone.

The following morning, I woke up tired and achy, with an extremely sore neck, and what felt like painful infections in both my ears and my bladder."

Another visit to Kendra's doctor on her return home confirmed her suspicions. But while a course of antibiotics took care of both the UTI and ear infections, she couldn't shake off the extreme lethargy and the dark moods that were now plaguing her. And then there were the infections. Week after week, Kendra found herself fighting one infection after another. Her physician was constantly referring her back to the hospital for bloodwork. Her white blood cell count was elevated. There was blood in her urine. But they couldn't identify any bacterial cause. She was tested for parasites and other infections that she might have picked up in Mexico. She had trouble breathing, so they X-rayed her lungs, but found nothing. Everyone was baffled. If they couldn't pinpoint a cause, they couldn't treat it. All they could do was send her home with antibiotics and instructions to take ibuprofen for the pain. After several months of this, Kendra felt completely lifeless and utterly devoid of hope.

Then, one day, following another fruitless visit, one of the team took another look at the bloodwork that had been run several weeks before. Lo and behold, Kendra had tested positive for mononucleosis, which is caused by the Epstein Barr Virus. Finally, she had a diagnosis and an explanation for at least some of the symptoms she was suffering. But while the mystery had been partly solved, Kendra was still suffering.

She was following the hospital's protocol to the letter, drinking plenty of water, resting, and taking ibuprofen to control the pain. But she still didn't feel any stronger. Every part of her body ached, she felt sore all over, and the physical weakness made her feel like an old, old woman. She had no energy and couldn't even walk to the mailbox anymore. The worst part was that without a real diagnosis to explain what was causing her symptoms, Kendra's husband and her doctor were beginning to question whether it was all in her mind. Frustrated, exhausted, and unable to accomplish much of anything, she was close to the point of giving up. Life was no longer worth living. She just wanted to die and be with her dad.

Pushed to the edge, Kendra set up one last-resort appointment with her exasperated physician. Her confidence in finding a solution was zero, but she needed to tell someone that she had reached rock bottom, and was ready to give up on life. It was during that visit that one of the nursing assistants told Kendra about the Life Center and the Harmonic Egg. Even though she was uber-skeptical, Kendra knew she had nothing to lose. She called the Center to make an appointment before she had even left her physician's parking lot. And right from the very first session, her perspective shifted dramatically.

"When I arrived at the Life Center, I was a bit nervous, still not sure if the treatment was legit, and pretty convinced that I had just wasted a bunch of money. I hadn't slept properly in ages, so I certainly didn't expect that I would nap in the Egg. But I did. Even weirder, to me, was that I couldn't stop crying, but there was absolutely no emotion behind the tears; they just kept streaming down my face. And I couldn't stop yawning. I didn't know what was happening, whether I was just releasing months of exhaustion, but for the first time in a long time, I felt a glimmer of hope... and confidence that Gail knew what she was doing and could help me get better. That was all I needed. From that moment on, I was hooked, and I immediately scheduled five weekly appointments.

The very next morning I woke up around 6:30, without an alarm clock and with energy! I put on my walking shoes and headed out the door for a morning walk—a morning ritual for most of my life before getting sick. As I stepped out the front door and took a few deep breaths of the fresh crisp air, I teared up with joy! It felt like I had entered heaven and was finally free! I walked an entire mile that day, and gradually worked my way up to a slow jog over the following week. With great excitement I shared the wonderful news with Gail! While happy for me, she warned me not to overdo it.

After my second session in the Egg, I felt empowered to start running again. Before my third appointment, I had made my way back up to a three-mile run. I told Gail that I was healed and no longer needed to work

on destroying the mono virus, but instead, could work on grief from my
father's death. Gail, in her wisdom, advised we continue working on the
mono, but also add a light color in the Egg to address grief. Once again,
I woke up the next morning feeling fantastic. After finishing my fifth
treatment, I purchased the monthly membership package, knowing that I
never wanted to go back to being sick again!!"

Within a short time, Kendra began to show signs of recovery. Her appetite
and energy returned, she started to feel a renewed sense of well-being and
started exercising again. But Kendra wasn't out of the woods yet.

A few months later, a broken and infected tooth led to an emergency
root canal, after which her personality underwent a change. And for a time,
it looked as if her health had completely regressed. The temporary metal
screw the dentist had placed in her mouth in preparation for an impending
implant was causing more pain than it should. Her anxiety and depression returned, and once again, she was experiencing extreme lethargy and
suicidal thoughts. Kendra didn't like taking medication, but she knew she
needed help. She consulted a psychiatrist, who placed her on another low-
dose anti-depressant, which gradually began to have a positive effect. Still,
the pain in her mouth continued to be a problem, even though her dentist
repeatedly reassured her that they had failed to find any cause.

Then one day, the cap on the metal post in Kendra's mouth popped off
of its own accord.

"You'd better come in," the dental hygienist advised. "It's not a big deal,
we'll just screw it back in."

Unfortunately, what should have been a simple routine procedure
turned into one of the scariest and most painful experiences of Kendra's
life. What the X-Rays had not revealed was that the bone was beginning
to attach itself to the metal post. In trying to remove it, the hygienist
accidentally ripped out a chunk of flesh. Kendra screamed. Blood gushed
from her mouth. Panic ensued. And when they finally stopped the flow,
they discovered the existence of a deeply imbedded infection, which
required yet another course of antibiotics.

When Kendra told me about this incident on her next appointment, I
explained to her that acupuncturists and an increasing number of health
practitioners believe that each tooth is associated with a specific organ in
the body. And that infection and pain in a tooth can predict problems in
those related organs and systems. I showed her a Meridian Tooth Chart,

which illustrates the empirical relationship between teeth and body organs. I told her that when a tooth becomes infected or diseased, the organ(s) or body parts on the same acupuncture meridian can also become unhealthy. Likewise, dysfunction in a specific organ can lead to a problem in the corresponding tooth.

Since Chi (energy) flows along the body's meridian lines in both directions, injured teeth can be a symptom of problems in a body part. For example, the lower central and lateral incisors are on a meridian connected to the adrenal glands, so sensitivity or pain in these teeth may indicate an imbalance in adrenal function. A root canal in your second bicuspid (tooth 4) may affect the thyroid, lungs, or liver. It can also affect the shoulder or big toe. Proof again that everything is connected!

I explained to Kendra that infections under the teeth may be undetectable on X-Rays, especially in root canal-treated teeth. When toxins leak from these infections, they can depress the normal functions of the immune system, causing systemic diseases of the heart, kidney, uterus, and the nervous and endocrine systems. Toxins can also seep out of root canals when an imperfect seal allows bacteria to grow and undergo changes. Many of my clients get thermal imaging to check for infections in the body.

When we checked the tooth in question on the meridian chart, it was connected to the lungs, heart, and immune system. It also showed depletion in vitamins. The latter was confirmed when we looked at Kendra's most recent bloodwork. When she asked if I thought she should go ahead with the implant, I told her that it had to be her decision. But if it were me, I wouldn't have any metal put into my mouth as we don't really know what it does to the body. Kendra refused the implant. While she is still choosing to take her low-dose anti-depressant to support her emotional well-being, she feels that her regular sessions in the Harmonic Egg have enabled her to finally start processing the immense grief she felt at her father's passing:

"Looking back, I can see that a lot of what was going on with me was due to all the stress and the built-up grief and emotions. When Gail changed the colors of the light and the music to help with that, I actually started feeling a little bit of joy again. When I told my mom about it, she booked a session too and it did the same for her.

I really feel that Gail saved me. The antidepressants and anti-anxiety meds have supported my emotional well-being. But as far as the rest of my body is concerned, my immune system, the enervating weakness, the infections after the root canal, I don't know that I would have ever started feeling better physically without the Egg, because I just wanted to give up. Every time I go in the Egg, I leave feeling that I have much more energy. She not only believed me when no one else did, but she had so much confidence in the Egg and its ability to help my body begin to heal itself, that she helped *me* believe that I could get through this. The fact that she cared so much about me made me care about me again."

If you would like to see a meridian tooth chart, you can find many on the Internet and some have interactive charts.

Dr. Dana's Story

"Blasted Into the Stratosphere in the Harmonic Egg."

DR. DANA ANGLUND is an osteopathic physician with a practice in Denver, Colorado, who has developed his own energy healing modality called Divine Still Point. Dr. Anglund teaches other physicians, medical students, and healers about many aspects of energy healing and integrative medicine.

Though I initially met him through his interest in frequency-based healing modalities, he experienced both the light box and the Harmonic Egg. While testing the light box, Dr. Anglund had a pleasant experience and then fell asleep. When he awoke, he heard a click. He discovered that a bony restriction in his upper back that he had been unable to address through other therapies had opened.

Immensely relieved, Dr. Anglund was sold on the light box. He quickly embraced the Harmonic Egg, too, saying that the problem in his upper back was continuing to improve with each session. Prior to his experience in the light box, Dr. Anglund said his upper back had been locked down:

> "Nothing would open it, nothing would move it. But after continued sessions in the Harmonic Egg, even though it occasionally tightens up, I can move it myself just by changing my posture. So,while it's not completely gone, it's nothing like it was."

Relieved and delighted, Dr. Anglund now recommends the Egg to patients that he feels could derive the most benefit from it:

> "The way I explain it to my patients is that the first time I sat in there, as soon as the music started, I was immediately blasted into the stratosphere. I mean, it's just you feel like you're floating, and your consciousness is expanded, and yet there's no anxiety or worry, like all that stuff just kind of melts away ... it seems like there's an expansion, and it's comfortable, and peaceful, and yet very expansive. My patients are having positive experiences with the Egg. They frequently report feeling relaxed and energized while in it, and often feel immediate relief from pain and other

chronic issues, both during their time in the Egg as well as over a period of time afterwards. I had one patient who was struggling with chronic Lyme and co-infections, and was seriously considering reducing everything in her life, including her career and the amount of movement she did.

I recommended the Harmonic Egg as part of an integrative treatment protocol. When I saw her recently for an unrelated issue, she told me that she's starting a new career *and* a new exercise program. 'Now, I'm not just surviving. I'm actually thriving, and growing, and changing, and adding things to my life,' she declared. Which was a near miraculous turnaround for someone who was chronically sick and whose life was falling apart. That was probably the most dramatic change I've seen.

Based on my own personal experience, as well as the experiences of my patients, I believe the Egg has a beneficial effect on the whole person, positively affecting all aspects of the body and the mind. I work on the five energy bodies, so I look at the physical, the energetic, the mental, the intuitive, and the spirit bodies. The Harmonic Egg does all of that without thinking. It impacts the entire being, and it does it in such a way that is gentle and has limited, if not zero, side effects. And as a physician, as a healer, and as a human, that's what I'm looking for."

Christine's Story

"Vibrational Medicine."

CHRISTINE SULLIVAN, PhD., FNP-BC, is a healthcare practitioner who has over 30 years of experience. Her integrative approach to treating chronic pain and cognitive behavior issues and establishing mental balance utilizes a variety of treatments to facilitate long-term change to ensure patients enjoy full, happy lives, and physical and mental health.

Christine teaches necessary living and coping skills to those suffering the effects of postpartum depression, anxiety, and stress. Through her positive coaching methods, she has changed many lives for the better.

She is also skilled in managing symptoms of gynecological problems, including endometriosis pain, pelvic pain syndrome, hormonal changes of pregnancy and menopause, and premenstrual dysphoric disorder.

Christine has made it her life's mission to guide each of her patients to a more positive lifestyle filled with fulfilling relationships and optimal health and wellness balance. She fully believes in healing oneself from the inside out.

I met Christine in November 2018. Intrigued by the Harmonic Egg, Christine visited my website, where she read some of the testimonials from clients about their healings from the energy of light and sound. Christine worked with an MD, Dr. Salada, who was planning to be in Denver for the weekend. Christine told Dr. Salada about the Harmonic Egg, and suggested Dr. Salada might want to experience it. On hearing how much Dr. Salada had enjoyed her experience, Christine and her partner, Dr. Robert Young, MD, were curious to try it themselves. Here's what Christine had to say about her experience:

"In my practice of nursing, medicine, and clinical hypnotherapy, I hear so many stories of stress and disharmony in both physical and emotional existence. I felt that Gail's creation, with Tesla's claims of the geometry, including 3-6-9, and 12, may have some spiritual significance. I also felt that the secluded chamber seemed to be a private space for listening and reflecting, and I wanted to feel what this might be about. Since I'm a 'go, go' kind of person who always has too much to do, I wondered if I could sit still for my own quiet time.

At the time, I had a slight viral infection, and I felt that the mucous was being triggered lying back in the Egg, but after a while, the music seemed to calm down my response. Then I simply relaxed and felt I could have stayed in another half hour. My first session was comprised of an abbreviated 25 minutes of music, followed by five minutes of quiet solitude. After that session, the peristalsis of my irritable bowel functioned normally for eight weeks. After my second and third sessions, I noticed a calm sense within my being, in contrast to my reflex of feeling a little internal agitation with some patient encounters.

I had read several books about energy medicine and the vibrational aspects of rebalancing the meridians. I had no idea there was so much scientific evidence in energy medicine that was not mainstream enough for those of us in everyday patient care to be aware of. After my third session, we decided to buy the Harmonic Egg for our Center in La Jolla, California and incorporate sessions in the Egg with our hypnotherapy practice for our patient's well-being. We wanted, as medical professionals, to allow patients to know that we endorse alternative, non-pharmaceutical therapeutic options. We also plan to conduct our own research."

Together with her practice partners, Dr. Elizabeth Salada, and Dr. Robert Young, Christine wrote the following letter to explain to their colleagues and patients their philosophical perspective on the Harmonic Egg experience.

Vibrational Medicine

As physicians, nurse practitioners, nurses and other health care practitioners, we often feel that our traditional medical model of care does not achieve the healing outcome that our patients expect. After multiple changes of prescriptions, or complex polypharmacy combined with other traditional medical treatments, sometimes we feel we have reached an impasse in our role as medical or nursing "healers."

Numerous studies in energy medicine support the perspective that energy stimulates healing in the body, mind, and spirit in a natural way. Research in physics, molecular biology, and biomechanical functions suggest that energy and consciousness within our human body affects our emotional and physical responses. The stress response is well known in medical science to disrupt our internal homeostasis. Holistic healing embraces our personal belief system to release blockage of the natural flow of chemical and electrical signals (energy) that are essential for our well-being. "Life and health are dependent on the proper balance of metabolic, electrical, and light-energy flow throughout the cells of our bodies' and organs," says Dr. Richard Gerber, M.D., author of the book, *A Practical Guide To Vibrational Medicine.*

"The day science begins to study non-physical phenomena; it will make more progression in one decade than in all the previous centuries of its existence. If only you would know the magnificence of 3, 6 and 9, you would have a key to the Universe." wrote Nikola Tesla. "The 3, 6, 9 sequence plays an enormous role in life—the roles of continuance, survival, repetition, variation, pattern, reflection, communication, creativity, responsibility, emotion, and love." (*https://www.creativenumerology.com/nikola-teslas-astonishing-numbers/*).

The Harmonic Egg is a large hollow wooden chamber designed using Tesla's numbers, 3, 6 and 9, to create a geometrically balanced dodecahedron (12 sided on the outside) Egg. Within this chamber; light, frequency, vibration and sound create a blended energy to stimulate one's autonomic system to reorganize and promote homeostasis. Additionally, the Harmonic Egg allows for a subtle energy shift as one is induced to a deep state of relaxation. It is within the privacy of peaceful solitude one can emotionally let go of stress/trauma and allow for the effective rebalancing of our physical disruption. This experience may promote a broader perspective of one's existence within the reality of the Universe of energy and how it may help one heal.

Although as providers we may never know where disruptions occur within the body, our emotions and physical manifestation of imbalance are overtly revealed in symptoms, emotionally and physically. The peacefulness felt within the geometry of the Egg chamber allows for a holistic realignment of the body's energy as light and sound flows around and through the body. This natural meditative relaxation is risk free, and has no side effects compared to pharmaceutical agents. Numerous studies since the early 1900's have shown that non-invasive use of light and sound exists as a form of energy or frequency medicine. This therapeutic use of light and sound is defined as vibrational energy medicine (the new science is being called frequency medicine), and now is a viable option for those frustrated and suffering from what may be regarded as failed medical interventions.

Most, if not all, who have experienced the Harmonic Egg, report a remarkable feeling of peacefulness. We can all transcend to our higher consciousness to be active in our role to believe in our own natural ability to achieve or maintain our emotional and physiologic balance.

Scientific contributions from neuroscience, molecular biology, and physics are now actively supporting energy or frequency medicine as a legitimate alternative. Some also feel that energy medicine or frequency has the potential to change the trajectory of medical care in the future. The physician, known in our society as the dominant persona of the "healer," is encouraged to be open minded to embrace alternative therapies that may benefit patients.

As medical professionals, we invite you to experience a session in the Harmonic Egg so that you can share your experience with patients, family, friends and colleagues. The unique synergy of light and sound is so remarkable! We feel a passion to expand its availability to help those suffering from a wide range of conditions, feeling they have exhausted all options, and are frustrated with traditional medicine options. Now, as physicians and health care providers of varied disciplines, we can support our patients if we expand our consciousness to be willing to try for ourselves the peacefulness of vibrational energy/frequency medicine... The Harmonic Egg Experience!

Dr. Richard Gold

"Energetic, Emotional, and Spiritual Blockage Release."

DR. RICHARD GOLD is a licensed acupuncturist and holds a Doctorate in Psychology. Since graduating from the New England School of Acupuncture in 1978, he has devoted his professional career to studying, practicing, researching, teaching and publishing in the field of East Asian Medicine, and pursuing advanced studies in China, Japan, and Thailand.

Dr. Gold co-founded the Pacific College of Oriental Medicine, a regionally and nationally accredited college of Traditional Chinese Medicine with campuses in San Diego, Chicago, and New York City. He serves on the college board and continues to teach.

The author of *Thai Massage: A Traditional Medical Technique*, Dr. Gold has also worked in the field of applied neuroscience and sound. He is the president and executive producer of Metta Mindfulness Music, which is a company devoted to creating original music to facilitate meditation, health, and mindfulness, founded with Yuval Ron. When Yuval Ron told Richard Gold about his experience in the Harmonic Egg, Richard immediately made arrangements to explore the Egg himself. Here's what he had to say about it:

> "I'm fascinated with sound and its healing potential, and having followed Tesla's work since college days, Yuval's experience in the Harmonic Egg instantly resonated deeply with me.
>
> Having heard Yuval talk about his experience of hearing his music in the Egg, I decided to listen to the "Element of Wood" track from our Ancient Wisdom and Modern Sounds for Health and Healing CD. I've listened to our music compressed on MP3s, but it was rare for me to have the opportunity outside of Yuval's studio to listen to it full spectrum. So, there I was, in the zero-gravity chair, feeling comfortable and relaxed and the session is progressing. I could feel myself slowing down, going deep. My thoughts were slowing, and all of a sudden, I was having this experience where the sound was emanating from inside me out my ears. It was so shocking that I sort of came back into critical mind, and thought *That was unusual. Did I imagine that?* I went back

174

into the quiet again, and it happened again... the sound felt as if it was coming right through me and exiting my ears. Time seemed completely distorted too. As the session progressed, I found myself coming in and out, in and out, like with meditation, when you come out and think "Oh, I'm meditating," and then boom, you're out. But it was pretty easy to plug back into that meditative state.

When I emerged from the Egg, I felt clear-headed and communicative. But I didn't want to drive straight away. I didn't feel spaced out; I just wanted a little time to 'come back down.'

Later, as I was pondering what had happened, I wondered if the vibrations of the music had entered not just my ears, but through all of the cells in my body, and then merged with the sound coming in. It seemed to me that this might be part of the Egg's healing power; that it enters the meridians and the auric field, and then into the physical energy field—the meridians—and then connects to the brain. So, it's coming through the auditory system into the brain and from the body to the brain. It gave me the sense that Gail has really arrived at something unique and special with this environment.

I felt that the shape it invokes is an extraterrestrial image to a degree, and, on further reflection I do think it is somewhat of a transporter, not necessarily to other dimensions or other realities, but definitely outside of ourselves. I feel it helps facilitate that ability, like in meditation, to step back, observe, and listen to the voices, and realize that's not your true self. It seems to have the ability to act like a capacitator, an enhancer, and a little bit of a voyager. I can see how, to people who have vivid imagery and out-of-body experiences, it will be like an accelerator.

That experience inspired the idea of working directly with Gail to create not just the music, but meditative journeys. She had certain specifications of issues she wanted to deal with that we have designed through elements and doshas. And so, we immediately started working with the pattern of threes, sixes, and nines, and started weaving together some existing themes directed towards the main areas of problems that Gail wanted to address. Personally, I would like to go in it as often as I can."

Color Meanings, Associations & Benefits

Science has proven that we all respond emotionally, psychologically, and even physically to colors. As we learned earlier, color therapy can help to re-balance the subtle energy bodies and emotions by re-balancing the chakras. The colors described below are the same seven colors Sir Isaac Newton, after passing white light through a prism in the mid-1600s, named as being analogous to the notes of the musical scale. These seven colors are claimed to work not just through every cell of the body, but also to influence our consciousness, soul, and spirit.

Alongside each color below, I have listed the personality characteristics, chakras, health conditions, and symptoms that each relates to. This is not a complete list of what is possible with colors. There are shades like pink, magenta, lemon, and others that also have specific qualities for healing. Everyone is different and, therefore, will respond differently to color therapy. The purpose of this guide is to get you excited about how color can be a factor in your daily life, from the clothes or accessories you wear to the foods you eat. It is based on my experience with what has worked with clients, both in as well as out of the Harmonic Egg. As with everything, however, you will find conflicting information from various "experts." None of it is necessarily wrong, it's just a different school of thought, and a different perspective based on individual therapists' experiences of what has proved successful in their practices.

A WORD OF CAUTION. Please note that the information provided here is offered as a guide only to bring peace, joy, and vitality into your life. If you are seeking support with any physical, emotional, or psychological condition or ailment, I recommend you seek the counsel of a professional trained in providing color healing.

Red

The color red has the most extended length in the visible spectrum and the lowest rate of vibration. It is known as the "Great Energizer." It is a passionate and warm color that has a stimulating effect—both mentally and physically. It is associated with excitement, power, confidence, energy, and vitality, and the general excitement of life, and with will power, aggressiveness, nervousness, vigor, and force. Red's uplifting effect helps combat lethargy and laziness. It is effectively used wherever there is a lack of vitality, congestion, or constriction. Red relates to the root chakra and sex organs. Its function is to connect us to our roots, to ground us, and provide a firm foundation to all other energy centers in our body.

Positive Benefits

- Increases circulation/energy
- Helps alleviate rheumatoid arthritis
- Stimulates sluggish intestines
- Generates body heat (increases blood pressure)
- Stimulates ovulation and menstruation
- Is excellent for anemia and blood-related conditions
- Stimulates all the senses
- Builds red blood cells/hemoglobin builder
- Heals cold burns (frost, x-rays, UV)
- Stimulates arteries, kidneys, liver and genitals

Red Should Be Avoided When:

- With any condition that should not be stimulated
- High blood pressure
- When experiencing anger or overly excited
- When fever is present
- In cases of hypertension
- With nerve inflammation (neuritis), mental illness or more severe mental imbalances
- Autism
- If you have red hair, use the color red with caution

Orange

Orange is the color of sensuality, passion, and joy. It enhances mental and physical energy, stimulates creativity, and is used to help balance problems with the kidneys, large and small intestines, lower spine and sacroiliac joints. Orange is associated with resourcefulness, confidence, success, and sociability. And it is said to help remove inhibitions and encourage enjoyable relationships.

Orange governs the spleen chakra, which is also known as the sacral chakra. It is the seat of our creativity and allows us to enjoy the sensual pleasures in life.

Positive Benefits

- It is used therapeutically to heal grief
- Alleviates depression
- Eases chronic fear
- Improves social confidence
- Joyfulness
- Builds and stimulates liver function
- Stimulates creative thinking and enthusiasm
- Stimulates the lungs, respiration, and digestion
- Relieves muscle cramps and spasms
- Stimulates the thyroid and stomach
- Bone growth
- Helps heal bruises
- Stimulates the production of milk in mammary glands

Yellow

Yellow is the color of pure energy. Hot, bright, and cheerfully optimistic, it symbolizes the sun. It helps stimulate intelligence, alertness, and inspire creativity in people who are feeling sluggish or lethargic. Yellow is associated with cheerfulness, mental clarity, wisdom, inspiration, and self-esteem, and with stimulating curiosity and interest. It is particularly recommended for people with skin problems. Yellow is associated with the solar plexus chakra, which is known as the "seat of the emotions" and your personal empowerment. It allows us to gain the inner strength to pursue our life goals.

Positive Benefits

- Alleviates depression (orange too)
- Detoxifies the mind and body
- Helps with skin problems
- Can be used for conditions of the stomach, liver, and intestines
- Speeds up digestion and assimilation, as well as the passing of stools
- It can support the pores of the skin by stimulating lymphocyte production, which activates toxin elimination

- Aids scarred tissue in healing itself
- Stimulates lymphatics
- Reduces swelling
- Infertility
- Stimulates appetite
- Speeds metabolism
- Can assist in lowering A1C levels in diabetes
- Tones muscles

Yellow Should Be Avoided When:

- Spleen issues are indicated
- In the kitchen, unless you want to stimulate the appetite.
- Overuse of yellow can cause insomnia and digestive issues

Green

Green is known as the master color, or balancing color, as it is associated with the pituitary, which is the master gland. The most common color in nature, green is connected with energy, vitality, growth and renewal, hope, youth, and an enthusiasm for life. It promotes feelings of relaxation, restfulness, trust, comfort, contentment, harmony, and equilibrium. It is particularly beneficial for the heart, lungs, and circulatory system.

Green governs the heart chakra, the center of unselfish and unconditional love. It is a color that is said to flow from nature and the universe through the heart chakra, and with the power of love helps one to heal on the emotional and physical level.

Positive Benefits

- Facilitates peace, love, and harmony (helps with forgiveness)
- Enhances rest, relaxation, calmness, and stress reduction
- Can assist in balancing the hormones
- Increases immunity
- Builds up muscles, bones, and tissues
- Strengthens the nervous system
- Helps to eliminate ulcers
- Infertility

Green Should Be Avoided When:

- Excessive use can cause headaches

Blue

Blue is an essential healing color as it is linked with serenity, truth, and harmony, and has a relaxing effect on the mind and the body. Because it is considered a "cold" color, blue can be used in all conditions that involve heat in the body. Hence it is suitable for cooling fevers, lowering blood pressure, inflammation, and rapid heart rates. It helps with sleep and is, therefore, an ideal color for calming hyperactive children.

Blue is specific to the throat chakra, which governs communication and self-expression. It helps you to express your thoughts and emotions verbally to bring your inner desires to material manifestation. Because of its connection to the throat, it helps with imbalances in the thyroid and parathyroid glands, as well as tension in the neck and shoulder areas.

Positive Benefits

- Light blue is considered more spiritual, dark blue more sociable
- Facilitates clear communication
- Eases chronic pain
- Alleviates insomnia
- Enhances confidence in speaking
- Aids in calming the mind (mental relaxation)
- Cools down inflammations (don't forget rheumatic inflammations)
- Reduces Fever
- Reduces high blood pressure (Red increases blood pressure)
- Stops bleeding
- Relieves headaches
- Calms strong emotions like anger, aggression or hysteria
- Brings tranquility
- Eases sore throats
- Acts as an anti-irritant (for instance redness of the skin)
- Soothes emotional and mental suffering
- Stimulates the pineal gland
- Stimulates the parasympathetic system
- Enhances endurance
- Blue can be used for any type of ailment associated with speech, communication, or the throat. It is excellent for laryngitis or inflammation of the larynx
- Activates the pineal gland
- Alleviates migraine

- Reduces inflammation in colitis

Blue Should Be Avoided When:

- There is mild or severe depression

Indigo

Indigo is considered a "cold" color, and as a result, can be used in all conditions involving heat in the body. It enhances serenity, stillness, understanding, wisdom, devotion, imagination, awareness, intuition, accurate perception, courage, and higher intuition. Indigo has a relaxing effect on the mind and body.

Indigo is specific to the brow, or "third eye" chakra. Thus it is helpful with imbalances in the pineal and the pituitary glands, the sinuses, eyes, ears, and nose, and also with learning disabilities. The energetic qualities that indigo brings through the third eye chakra will help you develop your spiritual perception, gain trust in your intuition and insights, and enhance your clairvoyant, clairaudient, and clairsentient abilities.

Positive Benefits

- Helps reduce a rapid heart rate
- Is an excellent purifier of the bloodstream
- Benefits mental problems
- Acts as a sedative
- Relieves pain
- Reduces swelling

Violet

Violet is a "cooler" color, so it has a soothing and calming effect. It enhances our sense of self as a spiritual being with feelings of compassion and creativity. Like purple, and its related shades, lilac, and lavender, violet is connected with spirituality, and is therefore associated with perception, higher consciousness, intuition, and insight. It is also associated with creativity, beauty, inspiration, selflessness, generosity, and enhanced artistic ability.

Violet is specific to the crown chakra, so it is linked with the cerebral and nervous systems and mental functions. It is useful to help with imbalances in the pineal and the pituitary glands.

Positive Benefits

- Alleviates melancholy, hysteria, delusions and alcohol addiction
- Slows down an over-active heart
- Reduces eye inflammation
- Stimulates the spleen and the white blood cells (immunity)
- Soothes mental and emotional stress
- Helps in detoxification
- Expands Blood vessels
- Induces sleep
- Helps build leucocytes
- Epilepsy
- Concussion
- Neuralgia
- Lowers body temperature

Caution and Contraindications

Color therapy is one of the most ancient healing therapies. When used wisely and respectfully, it can help harness the energy of the sun's light to boost your body's natural healing ability. However, it's important to understand that while colors can heal, they can also harm. The use of white light in chronic conditions is dangerous, as white contains all colors. A chronically ill person's body cannot properly sort out or select the required frequencies from the white ray. Red light *increases* blood pressure and blue *decreases* it, even when the subject is blindfold. (Maybe that's why we get so irritated waiting for a red light to turn green?!)

Other Uses of Color

- Research shows that when gray industrial machines were painted orange, the morale of factory workers improved
- Black bridges painted green reduced suicide jumpers significantly
- In hospitals, oranges and yellows were proved to help patients get well faster
- In sports, blue-painted dressing rooms are regarded as conducive for resting, while red-painted rooms are considered best for "fight" talks

NOTE: Some organizations paint the opposing teams' dressing rooms blue, to give the home team the advantage!

Fast food restaurants use stimulating colors such as reds and yellows, as these are known to speed up eating. Yellow also has a stimulating effect on the appetite, thereby encouraging people to eat more.

Banks like to use neutral and cooling colors like greens and blues. Companies spend billions on selecting the right colors to use in their logos and branding to convey a positive image and qualities they want their customers to associate with them—i.e., blue suggests stability, dependability, and trust, whereas green conveys peacefulness, growth, and health, etc. There's so much more to color than meets the eye, and the psychology of color as it relates to persuasion is one of the most interesting (not to mention controversial) aspects of marketing. Think about the colors of the signs as you drive around town, and how they make you think about the business that has chosen to use them.

Using colored light bulbs for short periods of time, covering your body in colored silks, or wearing colored clothing are helpful when you need an emotional or psychological boost. But if you're seeking treatment for specific physical symptoms, it is recommended you consult a certified color therapist or qualified practitioner.

Below is a fun chart, taken from the book *The Ancient Art of Color Therapy* by Linda Clark, which shows a sample of how color can replenish minerals for your body. It makes me wonder how many of us take supplements that are not easily absorbed, or properly utilized by our individual body types. In cases like these, we would either be wasting our money, or making our kidneys and liver work harder to process them. Wouldn't it be cool if choosing different colored clothes and accessories, or eating different colored foods could help to replenish our bodies of specific vitamin or mineral deficiencies? [92]

One final point to note for those who choose to wear black a lot—it is not helping your body.

Vitamin	Color
A	Yellow
B12	Red
Other B Vitamins	Red and Oranges
C	Lemon (yellow-green)
D	Violet
E	Scarlet (red-magenta)
K	Indigo (blue-violet)

Epilogue

I am a huge advocate for alternative and and natural healing, and also of knowing when too much is dangerous. So I want to leave you with a very important message: Too much of a good thing can be harmful. So, please, know and respect your limits.

Too much of anything can be harmful. And piling one alternative treatment on top of another, or taking too many supplements can hurt your body and organs. To ensure you are using a modality properly, you should inquire as to what the correct protocol is and follow the instructions given by the professional.

Too often, clients have confided that their schedules are so busy they try to cram all their complementary treatments into one day. Some call it a spa day, others call it their "Me" day. They take the day off and go for their massage, then follow that up with acupuncture and chiropractic, and whatever else they can fit in. That's not okay.

Many energy and bodywork modalities stimulate the body's detoxification process. If you cram more than one treatment into a day, you will double, triple, or even quadruple that process. Too much detoxification can be as harmful as too little. It makes more sense, and is much gentler on your body to spread your treatments over a period of days, weeks, or even months, to give it time to respond, react, and then recover its homeostasis.

Your body is a precious instrument. While I encourage you to enjoy all the lovely modalities that are now proving beneficial, it's important to give each modality the respect it deserves, and not cram one thing upon another before your body has had time to process and integrate what it has received. Honor your body, love it, and listen to it. It does and will communicate with you.

Likewise, honor the modalities you enjoy. Listen to your practitioner/healer. Ask them questions about the correct protocol to follow, and how long it should take for you to integrate the healing you've received. And be willing to participate in your own healing, to do your part of the work, and respect your body's limits.

A Final Word From Gail

I hope you enjoyed this book. There is so much more to write and share, but not enough space to accommodate it all. So, for now, let me leave you with these final thoughts to ponder.

The Harmonic Egg is so much more than what has been shared here. Given what I have noticed, both with my clients and myself, I genuinely believe that it has magical powers. Not "magic" in the "out-of-this-world-fairy-tale" sense of the word. But magic in that it appears to do things in a wondrous, multidimensional manner that science doesn't yet fully understand or know how to explain.

I understand that this may sound fantastical or "woo-woo" to some. But I know what I have witnessed and personally experienced. And it is authentic. During the testing of the prototype, I had an intense and crystal-clear experience of remembering my birth. I recalled specific details of the delivery room, and what was going on around me. All of which was later verified by my astonished parents. I cannot claim to know how or why this information came to me during that session in the Egg, I only know that it did.

Since that time, I have experienced many transformations. My dreams are more vivid and lucid and now incorporate more of my senses—touch, taste, smell, and hearing—than they did before. I have become more attuned to subtle energies. And my intuition is stronger and more effective. I have developed the ability to "read" people, and in some cases, know what they are thinking. I am so much calmer than I used to be. And I have noticed an on-going dismantling of patterns that no longer serve me. I am receiving more "downloads" of information. I don't know how I know what I know; I can only imagine it must be information gained in a past life, which I am now able to remember. Or, this information is coming from another dimension.

The Harmonic Egg isn't just for stress, or for healing our physical and emotional bodies. I believe that part of its purpose is to germinate seeds planted deep within us that are wanting to flourish. Time and again, I've witnessed clients transform after sessions in the Egg. It seems to be helping them connect with their true selves, allowing them to let go of old behaviors, responses, and "stories," and find their inner light as well as their path in life. In short, it is raising their vibrations and consciousness, enhancing their creativity, and enabling them to realize their true potential.

All of this tells me that the energy of the Egg is not just influencing us while we are in it. It remains with us when we leave. And it also influences others who come in contact with our energy field.

Setting intentions while in the Harmonic Egg is extremely powerful. Many clients do this when they want to manifest something in their life. Hence, it's often called the "Manifestation" or "Intention" Egg.

I encourage you to explore the Egg for yourself. You can use your smart phone to scan the QR code below, or just type the URL into a browser to visit our website and find the nearest location to you. As of this writing, the Egg is now in twelve locations throughout the USA from California to Georgia, and as demand for them is growing, more and more Centers are installing them. We hope to be announcing the first International Harmonic Egg installation soon.

If you should happen to be in Denver, Colorado at any time in the future, I hope you'll give us a call and schedule a session in the original Harmonic Egg, which, as you can imagine, is by now, very well-seasoned.

And if I am not traveling, it will be my pleasure to personally welcome you to the Life Center.

https://harmonicegg.com/locations/

Recommended Reading

Color Medicine: The Secrets of Color Vibrational Healing by Charles Klotsch

Detoxify or Die by Dr. Sherry A. Rogers

Feelings Buried Alive Never Die by Karol K. Truman

Lights Out by T.S. Wiley

Medical Medium by Anthony William

Soul Speak by Julia Cannon

Sounding the Inner Landscape by Kay Gardner

The Biology of Belief by Bruce Lipton

The Complete Book of Chakra Healing by Cyndi Dale

The Complete Guide to Sound Healing by David Gibson

The Healing Code by Alexander Loyd and Ben Johnson

The Secret Language of the Heart by Barry Goldstein

Who's the Matter with Me? by Alice Tuttle Steadman

The Ancient Art of Color Therapy by Linda Clark

The Secret Power of Music by David Tame

About the Author

GAIL LYNN was first exposed to sound and light healing while working in the film industry as an executive producer for a movie about Elvis Presley called *Protecting the King*.

When Gail's doctor diagnosed her with severe cardiovascular stress at the young age of 37, caused by an accumulation of stress from two challenging relationships and three successive and extremely competitive careers in the automotive and telecommunications industries, and then as a Hollywood producer, she knew that she had to find a radical solution to her health issues. Extensive research led her into the world of frequency medicine and light and sound technologies. After just a weekend of sessions with a non-invasive sound and light chamber, her Heart Rate Variability medical test showed the stress on her heart had significantly decreased. Unable to believe it could have been that easy, she continued sessions periodically for three years, during which a lifelong condition of chronic asthma disappeared, along with severe migraines that had been plaguing her for 23 years.

Determined to help others and open her own healing Center in Denver, Colorado, Gail simultaneously set out to uncover the ancient history and the modern science behind light and sound as healing therapies. Following a series of extraordinary synchronicities, which guided her to combine light and sound technologies with sacred geometry and Tesla mathematics, she developed a revolutionary immersive, resonance healing chamber called the Harmonic Egg, which is advancing frequency healing to an unimagined level. To find out more visit: **www.harmonicegg.com**

References

1. https://bit.ly/35rKX8d
2. https://bit.ly/2MRCLYn
3. https://bit.ly/2ZOlDYu
4. https://imdb.to/2tnWMyJ
5. https://bit.ly/2MQemCb
6. https://bit.ly/2ZMOTiB
7. https://aniwilliams.com
8. https://amzn.to/2FhQeEr
9. https://iammonline.com
10. https://noeticsi.com
11. Who's the Matter With Me, Alice Steadman - https://amzn.to/39Dw6uD
12. Karol K. Truman's Feelings Buried Alive Never Die - https://amzn.to/35mLIiG
13. Double Slit Experiment YouTube Video - https://bit.ly/2u9P5fQ
14. https://en.wikipedia.org/wiki/Double-slit_experiment
15. Molecules of Emotion, Candace Pert, PhD. - http://candacepert.com
16. Dr. Masaru Emoto - https://amzn.to/2FjJeHq
17. The Biology of Belief, Bruce Lipton - www.brucelipton.com
18. www.larrydosseymd.com and www.dosseydossey.com
19. https://bit.ly/39FGVMs
20. https://wb.md/36nbEw1
21. https://en.wikipedia.org/wiki/Ted_Kaptchuk
22. Verbal First Aid: Help Your Kids Heal from Fear and Pain and Come Out Strong, Judith Simon-Prager, PhD and Judith Acosta, LISW - https://bit.ly/37DHy7H
23. https://nyti.ms/2QmiiwF
24. www.deanradin.org
25. https://phys.org/news/2005-08-pain.html
26. https://bit.ly/35outh1
27. https://www.summitlighthouse.org/sound-the-energy-of-creation/
28. https://bit.ly/39F1kRS
29. https://bit.ly/2uhSGss
30. Dr. Royal Raymond Rife - www.royal-rife.com

31. Dr. James Gimzweski, Sonocytology - https://bit.ly/36nNaCL

32. Dr. Dominique Surel, https://noeticsi.com/about/

33. Fabien Maman - https://bit.ly/2rSLsKx

34. Dr. Dan Cohen - Music & Memory organization -
     https://bit.ly/37DRz4v

35. Dr. Larry Dossey - The Extraordinary Healing Power of Ordinary
     Things: Fourteen Natural Steps to Health and Happiness -
     https://amzn.to/2sBQyLN

36. Stuart Mitchell - https://yourdnasong.com/#tf-services

37. Drumming and the immune system - https://bit.ly/2QOF3bE

38. Jonathan Goldman - The Humming Effect - https://bit.ly/37AKbqS

39. Cymatics - https://www.delamora.life/cymatics/

40. Cymatics - https://bit.ly/36mAlIJ

41. Alexander Lauterwasser - https://bit.ly/2MTYX4a

42. Joan Ocean - https://www.joanocean.com/

43. Communicating with Dolphins - https://bit.ly/2sOmpbU

44. Diane Mandle - https://bit.ly/2QIuqXT

45. Didge Project - https://bit.ly/2QlIN5C

46. Dr. Jonathan Beaulieu - Music And Sound In The Healing Arts:
     An Energy Approach - https://amzn.to/2FimIyr

47. Barry Goldstein, The Secret Language of the Heart: How to Use Music,
     Sound, and Vibration as Tools for Healing and Personal Transformation
     - https://www.barrygoldsteinmusic.com/, https://amzn.to/2ZPKZFr

48. Don Campbell, The Mozart Effect - https://amzn.to/2QIDhsK

49. Oliver Sacks' Musicophilia, Tales of Music and the Brain, Revised and
     Expanded Edition - https://amzn.to/2trWPtl

50. Eileen Day McKusick, Tuning the Human Biofield, -
     https://amzn.to/2SQGqcB

51. Dr. Mitchell Gaynor's Sounds of Healing: A Physician Reveals the
     Therapeutic Power of Sound, Voice, and Music -
     https://amzn.to/37ALbv8

52. Daniel J Levitin - This is Your Brain on Music: The Science of
     A Human Obsession - https://amzn.to/37BVnmO

53. Anthony Holland - https://bit.ly/35oAwCe

54. Dame Evelyn Glennie - https://bit.ly/37B29tm

55. Alfred A. Tomatis - https://www.tomatis.com/en/alfred-tomatis

56. Barry Goldstein, https://www.barrygoldsteinmusic.com/

57. Dr. Donese Worden - https://drworden.com/

58. Yuval Ron - https://yuvalron.com

59. Dr. Richard Gold - https://inspirenationshow.com/inspire-443-yuval-
     ron-dr-richard-gold/

60. http://mettamindfulnessmusic.com/
61. Sandie Sedgbeer - http://omtimes.com/iom/shows/what-is-going-om/
62. Harmonic Egg Wellness Tracks - https://bit.ly/2FluyaI
63. The seed of life institute and SOLi school - https://bit.ly/36zJBcw
64. Raphael and the Golden Ratio in Modern Art - https://bit.ly/2ukjnwN
65. Drunvalo Melchizedek - https://www.drunvalo.net
66. https://www.phidle.com/blogs/sacred-geometry
67. https://bit.ly/2QJD2NV
68. https://www.jacobliberman.org
69. https://bit.ly/2ZQCcmP
70. Effects of light pollution, detailing effects on Human, animals, wildlife, energy & night sky - https://bit.ly/2txQJYj
71. http://www.discoveriesinmedicine.com/Enz-Ho/Finsen-Light.html
72. https://bit.ly/2FilPGj
73. https://bit.ly/2Fip1l5
74. Science Daily article Light as Medicine? Researchers Explain How https://bit.ly/2ZORY1q
75. Negative Effects of Infrared Waves - https://bit.ly/2ZWBsg4
76. The Nei Ching - https://bit.ly/2MUKOn2
77. https://en.wikipedia.org/wiki/The_Canon_of_Medicine
78. https://bit.ly/2ZZDU5z
79. Chromalive® Color Therapy Penlight Set - https://bit.ly/35oFkYd
80. www.Colorglasses.com
81. T.S. Wiley, Lights Out: Sleep, Sugar, and Survival - https://amzn.to/2uaAzo6
82. Julianne Bien - https://spectrahue.com/color-light-therapy-works/
83. Colorpuncture - https://colorpuncture.org/about/
84. Samassati Color Therapy - https://bit.ly/2QHGp88
85. Nikola Tesla - https://www.britannica.com/biography/Nikola-Tesla
86. Pythagoras - https://www.britannica.com/biography/Pythagoras
87. Vortex Based Mathematics - www.esotericonline.net/group/vortexmath
88. 5 Steps to Harness the Power of Intention by Deepak Chopra - https://bit.ly/36nAUCn
89. https://www.researchgate.net/scientific-contributions/William-A-Tiller-2120306459
90. https://suzymiller.com/
91. The Intention Experiment: Using Your Thoughts to Change Your Life and the World. By Lynne McTaggart - https://amzn.to/2tsCeoV
92. The Ancient Art of Color Therapy by Linda Clark - https://amzn.to/2MSqG5d